THE LOGIC OF RATIONAL THEISM

Exploratory Essays

Edited by

William Lane Craig

and

Mark S. McLeod

Problems in Contemporary Philosophy
Volume 24

The Edwin Mellen Press
Lewiston/Queenston/Lampeter

Library of Congress Cataloging-in-Publication Data

This book has been registered with the Library of Congress.

This is volume 24 in the continuing series
Problems in Comtemporary Philosophy
Volume 24 ISBN 0-88946-369-7
PCP Series ISBN 0-88946-325-5

A CIP catalog record for this book
is available from the British Library.

The Edwin Mellen Press
Box 450
Lewiston, New York
USA 14092

The Edwin Mellen Press
Box 67
Queenston, Ontario
CANADA L0S 1L0

The Edwin Mellen Press, Ltd.
Lampeter, Dyfed, Wales
UNITED KINGDOM SA48 7DY

Printed in the United States of America

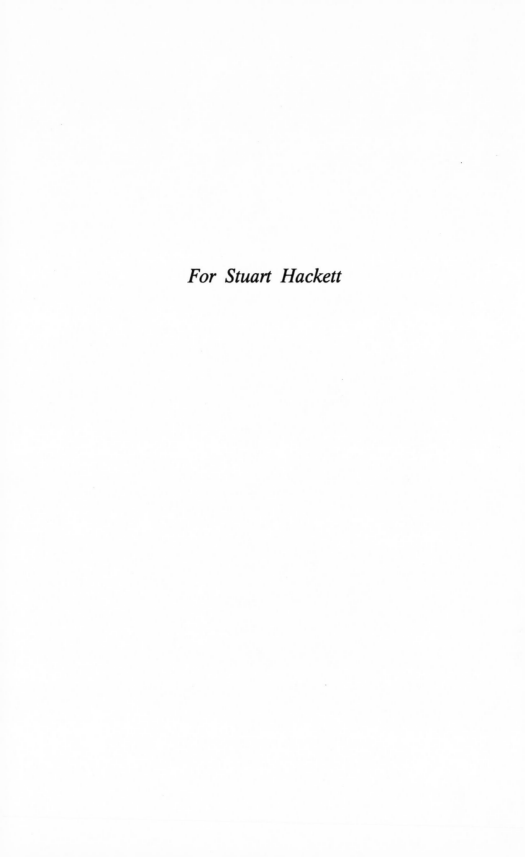

For Stuart Hackett

TABLE OF CONTENTS

III. THEISM AND THE WORLD

Preface

I

There's no denying it: Stuart Cornelius Hackett is an eccentric. What else can you say about someone who grows out his beard but shaves off his hair, whose sartorial tastes encompass wearing purple trousers with a red shirt and homemade vest, who sports a silver cross and a broad leather belt featuring a marijuana pipe buckle (a gift from his son which he wears upside down so as not to offend his seminary students), who talks naturally and extemporaneously about philosophical subjects in prolix, Germanic-style sentences so long that by the time he finishes one sentence his listener finds difficulty in remembering the main subject and the verb, who spends half a lecture period telling jokes and anecdotes, yet somehow manages to teach his students more about philosophy than any other professor they have heard, and who composes and sings hillbilly country music, which he resolutely accompanies with guitar and wailing harmonica? Yes, Stu is eccentric, and his students love him for it.

But as much as Stu's tonsorial and sartorial peculiarities delight them, so his earnest quest for truth inspires them. His breadth of knowledge of philosophy—West and East, historical and contemporary, in metaphysics, epistemology, and ethics—and his careful philosophical analysis and rigorous argumentation have served as models and goals to which his philosophy students have aspired. More than that, perhaps, he has inculcated the love of truth—of God's truth—in the minds of many generations of students who have sat under his tutelage.

For Stu is above all a Christian philosopher. He beautifully exemplifies the marriage of rigorous intellectualism with a vibrant, evangelical faith, *fides quaerens intellectum*. Well before it became customary on the American scene for the professional philosophical community to include Christians, or for the evangelical community to include philosophers, Stu was both a deeply committed Christian and an exacting philosopher, and these dual identities intertwine in his teaching, writing, and lifestyle.

No word of appreciation for Stu's work and example as a Christian philosopher would be complete, however, without mention of his wife Joan. She is the one who to some degree, at least, has helped to keep Stu's eccentricities in check (at her insistence, for example, he for many years acquiesced in the "absurd cultural habit" of wearing a necktie to class—though usually of the most outrageous sort, often made by his daughter), and it is she who supplies the social graces that oil their relations to colleagues and friends. One marvels sometimes at how two such opposite people could be as much in love and as mutually devoted to one another as they so evidently are. Their marriage is a wonderful example of what that relationship can and ought to be.

Over the years many of those students inspired by Stu's work and example have, of course, gone on to become philosophers themselves. In fact, all the authors of the essays in this volume were among those whom Stu taught at Wheaton, Westmont, or Trinity. The book thus represents a very personal word of thanks to Stu on the part of each one of us, his former students.

II

Our essays fall into three broad groups: religious epistemology, theistic arguments, and God's relation to human life, value, and the world. With respect to the first, contemporary epistemological thought has provided many tools for philosophers concerned with the epistemic status of religious belief. In the face of major challenges to classical foundationalism, philosophers have developed competing non-classical foundational and coherentist accounts of knowledge and rational belief. The epistemologist of religion need only apply these recent models to theistic belief in order to explore the possibilities for the rationality of that belief.

Alvin Plantinga, William Alston, and Nicholas Wolterstorff—some of the "Reformed epistemologists"—have done just that, each showing in his own way how beliefs about God may be rational without need of discursive justification in general or natural theology in particular. The essays in Section I seek to extend this program into two new areas and to clear up some muddles about the so-called "Reformed objection to natural theology."

Mark McLeod's contribution extends the spirit of the Reformed epistemologist beyond the notion of providing justification for theistic belief *simpliciter* to providing a framework from which one might develop a justification for the deep commitment theists typically have toward theistic claims. He uses some of Plantinga's work to spell out the criticisms of classical foundationalism and its relative, evidentialism. In developing a response to a proposed difficulty for Plantinga's position, he makes some observations about fundamental assumptions of rationality. He then suggests that the insights uncovered can best be accounted for in a holist approach to justification. The deep commitment toward theistic beliefs can be justified when justification is understood as having to do with the world-ordering power of such beliefs.

Jay Wood's essay seeks to extend the approach of the Reformed epistemologist beyond the justification of mere theistic beliefs to specifically Christian theistic beliefs and doctrines. The strategy of Wood's article is to contrast the evidentialist approach to justifying doctrinal beliefs (as opposed to more general theistic beliefs) with that of the Reformed epistemologist, and to evaluate the suggestion that doctrinal beliefs are properly basic (rational without discursive evidence). Wood notes several difficulties with Plantinga's general claims about properly basic beliefs and their relation to their grounding conditions and experiences. Perhaps the most telling of these is a challenge about specifying the conditions under which one is justified in forming a belief. Without specifying the details of this "input-output" relation, the Reformed epistemologist may be allowing for the proper basicality of "Great Pumpkin" beliefs, an eventuality the Reformed epistemologist will find infelicitous. Wood continues the discussion by articulating an account of how Reformed thinkers might understand the proper basicality of specific doctrinal beliefs such as "God is triune." Once arriving at this account, he suggests several problems with it, not the least of which is that Thomas Reid, from whom the Reformed epistemologists learned a great deal, would quite radically disagree with it. The Reformed response to this parting of the ways leads to other difficulties from which Wood draws the conclusion that although the Reformed strategy may be successful in allowing for permissive epistemic justification, it cannot do much in terms of a stronger positive epistemic status for the beliefs in question.

Stephen Evans's contribution serves to correct the misimpression that the adherent of Reformed epistemology finds no place for natural theology. He considers several reasons why Protestants are reluctant to appeal to the arguments of natural theology: the effects-of-sin argument, the reason-as-presumption argument, the superfluity argument, the god-of-the-philosophers argument, and the arguments-aren't-very-good argument. Each of these is evaluated in turn. Evans then argues that the best way to understand the theistic arguments is not as proofs but as rigorous presentations of "natural signs" that point to God. These signs fall into two kinds: signs evident in human nature and signs evident outside human nature. The former correspond to arguments such as the moral argument, while the latter correspond to arguments such as the cosmological argument. These signs are not enough when taken alone, but when taken with the work of God in one's life as faith develops, the signs can be helpful in making one's theistic beliefs rational. Hence natural theology is not essential for faith, but natural theology, or more broadly, evidentialist apologetics, can play a useful, if limited, role in "challenging the dogmatic assumption that we live in a closed universe" and can help to open people to the possibility of God's revealing Himself in a personal way to those who seek Him.

Evans's essay forms the natural bridge to Section II, in which theistic arguments are taken up. Concurrent with the rise of Reformed epistemology has been a vigorous resurgence of interest on the part of philosophers in the traditional proofs of God's existence. Once widely thought to have been laid permanently to rest by Hume and Kant, all of the theistic arguments have found vigorous, intellectually sophisticated, contemporary defenders. Already in 1957, Stuart Hackett had sought to proclaim their resurrection, presenting a sustained case for theism based on the cosmological, teleological, moral, and noetic arguments, but unfortunately his message fell on deaf ears. Today, however, many are listening. The four essays in this section examine some of the issues raised by current discussion of theistic arguments which Hackett himself has defended.

Robert Tad Lehe opens this section with an epistemological argument based on the coherence theory of truth. After formulating and defending that theory against typical objections, Lehe turns his attention to what is admittedly one of the most serious difficulties of such a theory, namely, that since it is impossible for us to discover or even approximate an all-embracing, perfectly coherent system, such a theory is useless as a regulative guide to truth. While conceding that we can never be sure that any particular belief we hold will in the end fit into the perfectly coherent system, Lehe nevertheless maintains that such uncertainty is inherent in any epistemological theory and need not undermine our confidence that sub-systems known by us to be coherent will be retained in the whole. He proceeds to argue that this perfect system, in order to serve as the end and guide of inquiry, must really exist—a mere, unrealized ideal is insufficient—and that there must, therefore, exist an omniscient Mind, or God, for whom the perfectly coherent system is a noetic reality.

In their contributions, William Lawhead and Robert Prevost present very similar objections to the cosmological argument for a temporal First Cause of the universe. By appealing to divine omniscience, they present a counter-example to the contention of the proponent of the *kalam* cosmological argument that an actually infinite number of things cannot exist. Lawhead argues that even if we adopt a theory of time according to which future events do not in any sense exist, still the orthodox theist (like Hackett) must grant that in light of God's foreknowledge, there exists in the divine mind an actually infinite number of items of knowledge corresponding to the potentially infinite series of future events. Similarly, Prevost maintains that if God knows particulars, then what for us appear to be potential infinites must be for Him actual infinites. Since the orthodox theist cannot abandon the doctrine of divine omniscience, the implication of both these essays is that the version of the *kalam* argument based on the impossibility of an actually infinite number of things fails. Whether this objection is telling will probably depend upon whether William Alston's independently suggested model of non-propositional divine knowledge, which Hackett appears to have anticipated, is acceptable. Since on such a model, God's knowledge is a simple intuition, which we finite minds fractionize into distinct propositions, His omniscience does not imply an actually infinite number of ideas or items of knowledge in the divine mind. One thereby gains all the advantages of the Thomistic model, yet without the disadvantages of a full-blown simplicity doctrine, which Hackett rejects. If such a model as Alston's is possible, then the force of the *kalam* cosmological argument would seem to be undiminished.

William Craig's essay on the Anthropic Principle and the teleological argument closes out this section. After summarizing recent scientific discoveries relevant to a "wider teleology" in nature, he analyzes the logic of the Anthropic Principle, according to which our surprise at the delicate balance of cosmological and physical conditions necessary to our existence ought not to surprise us, since if they were not so balanced, we should not be here to be surprised. Craig shows that such a principle is valid only in connection with a profoundly metaphysical vision of reality as a World Ensemble, a hypothesis no less extravagant than and in no sense superior to classical theism.

Section III opens with a paper by Stephen Bilinskyj on God's relation to the world in terms of His general providence, conservation, and concurrence. In dealing with this much neglected topic, Bilinskyj seeks to recover a Molinist theory of divine concurrence, according to which God acts, not *on* the secondary cause, but *with* the secondary cause to produce its effect. After expounding the advantages of the Molinist conception, he attempts to deal with the difficult question of precisely what it is that divine concurrence accomplishes over and above mere conservation of finite things in being.

Moving from the world to humanity, Pat Manfredi and Donna Summerfield inquire into the meaning of human life. Noting in passing the claim of Stace and Russell that if God does not exist then life is absurd, the co-authors are more concerned with the challenge posed by Thomas Nagel that life is absurd even if God exists, since our lives must be viewed from competing and apparently incommensurable standpoints. Manfredi and Summerfield argue that once the existence of God is granted, however, such differences in viewpoint on our lives that remain do nothing to prove that our lives are absurd. In the end, the residual "absurdity" amounts to the fact that we value certain concerns over the equally valuable concerns of others, which, as Manfredi and Summerfield point out, hardly constitutes a denial of life's meaning.

Ethical concerns on both a theoretical and practical level occupy the next three essayists. Mark Linville carefully analyzes the two horns of the Euthyphro dilemma concerning a theistic basis of ethics, with special attention to Kant's contributions to the discussion. Linville rejects both voluntarism and Platonism and seeks to find a way between the horns of the dilemma in Anselmian perfect Being theology. But his is no simple-minded escape; he shows that even on the supposition that the Good is to be understood in terms of God's moral nature, the same questions re-appear in new guise to haunt the theistic ethicist. But Linville argues that the very nature of ultimate criteria requires that those ultimate standards cannot themselves be evaluated in terms of their approximation to ultimate criteria. God's goodness is not, therefore, properly speaking a moral goodness resulting from His fulfilling a duty, but is a descriptive goodness, analogous to moral goodness in us, which consists in His being necessarily just, loving, merciful, generous, and so forth. In this way, God's good nature is the standard for what to us is moral goodness, and the Euthyphro dilemma is escaped.

Howard Ducharme's essay raises literal life-and-death philosophical issues that have profoundly important practical implications. He begins by explaining that classical Christian theism is committed to a dualist anthropology. He contends accordingly that the death of an individual is the passing away of the person, that is, of the rational, sentient, moral agent. He carefully distinguishes this metaphysical *definition* of death from a *criterion* of death, or some evidential standard which permits the inference that the person has passed away. Ducharme argues that irreversible loss of higher brain function is sufficient evidence that the person has passed away. In so arguing, Ducharme is less restrictive than the President's Commission, which maintained that the loss of function of the *whole* brain, including the stem, is necessary for death. The key question to be asked here is what justification supports the inference that the person has passed away when the higher brain alone has ceased to function. How do we know, given a dualist anthropology, that the immaterial substance has not yet passed away so long as the body continues to function, even if, as Ducharme points out, there is no possibility of future significant interaction between the two substances?

Our final contribution, from Glenn Hartz, deals with the ethical importance of desires. After showing that our desires play a key role in determining the moral status of certain emotions and attitudes, he raises the meta-ethical question of the basis of the moral status of our desires, emotions, and attitudes. Eschewing a consequentialist or deontological approach to this question, even within a theistic framework, Hartz turns instead to the ethics of virtue tradition, which in a theistic framework may take the form of either divine character virtue ethics or divine command virtue ethics, in order to argue that part of the moral status of mental states derives neither from consequences nor duties, but resides in the character trait itself as it mirrors or fails to mirror either God's character or commands. He closes with several practical suggestions about bringing one's character into line with the divine standard by embracing a master desire of pleasing God and following certain rules concerning, not what we do, but what manner of persons we are.

III

In addition to the authors who contributed philosophical essays to this *Festschrift,* Arthur Holmes wrote a warm and entertaining biographical essay about Stu. Our gratitude goes to Professor Holmes for his gracious addition to this work. Our thanks are also due Dean Blankenbaker of Westmont College for the generous financial assistance toward the typesetting and publication of the book and Dean Peterson of Trinity College for generous financial support of the volume's publication. We are grateful as well to Jan Craig for her production of the book in diskette form suitable for typesetting. Our thanks also to Ginny Murray of Murray Typesetting for transforming the text to an acceptable format for publication. For the two editors and Jan, this has been a labor of love.

William Lane Craig
Brussels
Mark S. McLeod
Santa Barbara

Stuart Hackett, Philosopher And Friend

One who eavesdrops on the nostalgic reminiscences of alumni soon learns of some professor whose learning, intellectual power, quick wit and distinctive ways have earned the respect and endearment of generations of students. Stuart Hackett is the example *par excellence* of such a person.

I first ran into Stuart in the spring of 1957. Attending a professional meeting at Covenant Seminary near St. Louis, wandering through the library on the way to breakfast, I passed this figure, pen at the ready, vehemently reading Sartre's *Being and Nothingness*. That anyone would wade through those hundreds of pages was remarkable enough, that it should be done before breakfast was even more remarkable, but that it should be done "vehemently" topped it all. His reading was punctuated with grunts and exclamations (which were which was unclear)—a habit I was to grow accustomed to overhearing years later when Stu occupied the next office to mine on the third floor east of Wheaton's Blanchard Hall. Later that day, in response to a paper I presented on a realistic theory of perception, he moved beyond grunts and exclamations: either my theory was a kind of epistemological monism or it was an epistemological dualism, for no other logical alternative can exist. Thence a disjunctive syllogism emerged, Stuart's characteristic form of argument.

Disciplined scholarly habits have constantly marked both his professional career and other aspects of his life as well. His devotional life has involved systematic use of the Greek and Hebrew texts of Scripture. His physical habits involve regular exercise:

long before jogging and health clubs existed, he was doing dozens of push-ups in early
morning hours. He used to carry a picture of himself as a young teenager, rather like
the fat boy in *Pickwick Papers,* as a reminder of what had been and could be again. On
a rare occasion when he accompanied some of us to an American Philosophical
Association meeting (for Stu despises leaving his wife to attend meetings), a group of
us sat talking one evening in our hotel room. We started kidding him about the exercises
he announced for early next morning. He retorted that he could do more push-ups than
the other five of us together. We took him on. He won.

But disciplined habits combine in him with depth of feeling and warmth of
relationship. "I love you all" is his typical farewell, and to this day I never speak with
him on the phone or in person without hearing (and feeling) some such expression. Stu
has his ways: one well-known figure described him as "odd, but in a nice sort of way,"
and it's this unique combination of "odd" and "nice" that people come to love. His
attire is hardly either professorial or in fashion. His hair remained crewcut decades
after crewcuts became passe: but that crewcut head with a bushy beard is Stu himself.
And he heartily enjoyed telling of the elevator operator in a Chicago department store
who took one look at it and declared, "Man, you got that head on upside down!"

Born November 2, 1925, Stuart Hackett lived in Binghamton, New York, until he
left for Wheaton College in 1943. It was there, in his freshman year, that he first met
his future wife, Joan Holsted, the daughter and granddaughter of missionaries to India.
The devoted couple with their three children have remained an unusually close family.
After only a year at Wheaton, however, Stu transferred to Cornell University where he
was enlisted in the Navy V-12 program. His lowest grade was a 71 in Naval
Organization, even P.E. fared better with 75; but the Cornell move proved providential,
for there he met and studied under philosopher E. A. Burtt, himself the child of China
missionaries, and whose book on *Types of Religious Philosophy* was a long-time
classic. Burtt turned Stuart on to philosophy. Graduating Phi Beta Kappa, he returned
in 1946 to the midwest; a term at Northern Baptist Theological Seminary and then an
M.A. program in Biblical Studies at Wheaton. His Wheaton transcript shows a straight
A record in all undergraduate and graduate courses taken there. The next three years
were spent at Syracuse University, working on a doctorate in philosophy that
culminated in a dissertation on the Indian philosopher Aurobindo Ghose.

Stu's teaching career began at the age of 26. By this time an ordained Baptist minister, he accepted a position at Western Conservative Baptist Seminary in Portland, Oregon. One of his students was George Mavrodes, now the well-known philosopher of religion at the University of Michigan. Mavrodes and the Hacketts have remained fast friends ever since. In 1955, a move came to the Conservative Baptist Seminary in Denver whose president Vernon Grounds exemplified for him "an enlightened Christian conviction tempered with deep Christian compassion."[1] Those two years in Colorado saw the completion of *The Resurrection of Theism*, a highly rigorous case for theism in a day when philosophical work among evangelicals was largely lacking. Unfortunately, the book did not receive the attention it deserved: it was by and large over the heads of any evangelical readership at that time. As Stu himself put it later,

> A quarter of a century ago, in the frenzied fervor and optimism of my youth, I wrote a book in which I discussed rather technical questions about religious knowledge and theistic metaphysics. Like Hume's Treatise, the book fell stillborn from the press because of its heavy style and technical context.[2]

Six years of seminary teaching were followed by 21 in Christian liberal arts education, first at Louisiana College, a Southern Baptist institution in Pineville, Louisiana. He found being a one-man philosophy department less than ideal, and in 1963 moved to Wheaton College. Here his teaching, in addition to sections of the general education Introduction to Philosophy course, included courses in philosophy of religion, Oriental philosophy, ethical theory, and occasional one-philosopher seminars. He loved having a good number of high ability students, and they loved him. His teaching was vigorous and his enthusiasm contagious: entering the classroom, he would close the draperies to eliminate distractions, take a sip of water from his green glass, clear his throat, and then lecture to get people sitting on the edges of their chairs. His methods rarely changed: "If it ain't broke, don't fix it" was his motto in the classroom as well as at home. He viewed teaching as having students listen in as he "did his thing." The classroom was his element. It gave him the same kind of experience

---

[1] *The Resurrection of Theism* (Chicago: Moody Press, 1957), p. 12.

[2] *The Reconstruction of the Christian Revelation Claim* (Grand Rapids, MI: Baker Book House, 1984), p. 13.

he gained from playing a country and western music concert. And play he did, occasionally as a classroom prank, but also with a student group called "Nashville West." The lyrics were often his own: corny, and hardly calculated to impress administrators—lyrics like "Wheaton Chapel Blues" and "The Little Brown House Out Back."

The Wheaton years proved philosophically enriching. He participated in two summer seminars, one led by William Frankena in 1966 on Ethics, sponsored by the Council for Philosophical Studies at University of Colorado, and an NEH one led by William Alston in 1978 at University of Illinois. In 1969, with grants from the Alumni Association and the Institute for Advanced Christian Studies, and accompanied by his entire family, he spent a year studying Hindu philosophy in India, taking in a conference at the East-West Center in Hawaii enroute. From September to April the Hacketts lived in Bangalore, and several benefits emerged: facility in reading Sanskrit (two years of part-time language study had been spent in preparation), reading of important source materials, identifying or purchasing other source materials, and a careful translation of some. His attention was focused on questions of religious knowledge and the relation of the phenomenal world to Ultimate Reality. Out of this work was eventually to emerge his second major work, *Oriental Philosophy: A Westerner's Guide to Eastern Thought.* But it was a frustrating year: living and travel conditions were, for such a highly structured person, frustratingly unpredictable and distracting. And on returning to Wheaton he found many of the sources for which he had gone all the way to India already available a short distance up the road at the headquarters of the Theosophical Society. For Joan, however, it was a journey back to childhood roots.

Meantime some professional papers appeared. In 1967, the *International Philosophical Quarterly* published "Contemporary Philosophy and the Analytic-Synthetic Dichotomy." In many ways it is typical of Stuart's work: a brief historical introduction, a schematization of competing views leading to critical analyses, and a final "emerging prospective" reflecting his own epistemology with its synthetic *a priori* principles. The article provided an excellent overview, and for a number of years I assigned it on the analytic-synthetic issue in my epistemology course. In 1969 *IPQ* published another paper, one he had presented at the Wheaton Philosophy Conference that featured Paul Ricoeur, this paper entitled "Philosophical Objectivity and Existential Involvement in the Methodology of Paul Ricoeur." Yet another appeared in 1972 in the E.A. Burtt *Festschrift*, and that same year he presented a paper on Ninian Smart's methodology at the Wheaton Conference that featured Smart himself. For a wider readership than these papers, he edited an anthology in collaboration with his former student George Mavrodes, *Problems and Perspectives in Philosophy of Religion* (Allyn and Unwin, 1967).

This professional activity doubtless contributed to invitations he began to receive to teach elsewhere. He declined a visiting appointment at Southern Illinois University at Edwardsville for 1971-72, but went to Westmont College in Santa Barbara in 1975-76. In 1978 he moved back to seminary teaching at Trinity Evangelical Divinity School. There his main activity has been with the M.A. program in philosophy of religion. Although this program was not central to the seminary's task, and the decision to phase it out disappointed Stuart greatly, the contribution it has made to the development of a new generation of Christians in philosophy is outstanding. His third major work, promised 30 years earlier,[3] emerged from teaching apologetics there and from the provision of a generous sabbatical program. *The Reconstruction of the Christian Revelation Claim* builds a case for the rational superiority over other views of a Christian view of general revelation, of Christ, and of Scripture. In the process, the book covers an array of topics with a great deal of good sense as well as philosophical rigor: the deity of Christ, the Bible and science, miracles, religious experience, ethical relativism. And in characteristic fashion he subjects alternative views to a serious critique. Thus the original overall project promised in *The Resurrection of Theism* has now found completion.

Stuart Hackett's basic philosophical beliefs are clear. He is first and last a theist, a Christian theist. He rejects both classical rationalism and classical empiricism in favor of a kind of "rational empiricism" with Kant-like synthetic *a priori* categories, modified by adding a divinely created preformation of the structure of thought to the structure of things. This makes possible the rational apprehension of things-in-themselves, overcoming the phenomenalism and scepticism often drawn from any dualistic epistemology. Natural theology is therefore possible, too, and causal-type arguments (cosmological, teleological, and moral) can be valid. At least this much persists without change throughout thirty years of Stuart's published work.

---

[3]*Resurrection*, pp. 10-11.

Faced with other philosophical views contradicting his own, the strategy is simple: an extended disjunctive syllogism:

Either A or B or C or D.
A and B and C are either self-contradictory or meaningless, therefore false.
Therefore, D.

And D, of course, is always Hackett's own position.

I recall back in the sixties pointing out the obvious objection that D will only seem certain until some smart-alec produces an E or F. This was readily granted, and Stuart added that in the *Resurrection* book he was too dogmatic about the finality of his argument. That realization is reflected in subsequent writings. His first book emphasized rational objectivity:

Indeed, if rational objectivity were really not attainable, even this judgment itself, that we are conditioned by our beliefs, would fall short of rational objectivity and would therefore be eliminated by its own assertion. From such a line of argument as this, it must be concluded that either rational objectivity is possible or else knowledge itself is impossible and we are reduced to absolute scepticism.[4]

In *Oriental Philosophy,* he still talks of objective, rational standards "in the sense that these principles do not depend on the special presuppositions of a particular viewpoint," but "a thinker's aim at objectivity may still be tainted with subjectivity. . . ."[5] After detailing ways in which this is so, he adds: "there are numerous non-rational factors . . . which both motivate and obstruct belief-commitments."[6]

In the *Reconstruction* book he goes further:

---

[4]Ibid., p. 10.

[5]*Oriental Philosophy* (Madison, WI: University of Wisconsin Press, 1979), pp. 6-7.

[6]Ibid., p. 11.

For a man's philosophy is the sum or collection of basic beliefs by which, consciously or not, he makes substantive decisions, guides his conduct, and directs his activities toward the fulfillment of significant ends. . . . With those beliefs, he will find himself at the very core of a perspective about the meaning of human existence—and that core will be the center of his philosophy.[7]

The emphasis therefore changes to "comparative rational plausibility." After summarizing his conclusions about the Christian revelation claim, he writes:

For the systematic exposition of all this as a philosophical perspective, I have claimed, from a human standpoint, no more than a comparative rational plausibility which I sincerely regard as involving a more adequate and comprehensive explanation of the meaning of existence than any analogous alternative explanation with which I am familiar.[8]

Philosophy has become a more personalized matter, hence less dogmatic (in Kant's sense of rationalist dogmatism), but none the less firmly convictional. This mellowing speaks well for Stu's consistency. He recognized the influence of others on his thinking. He recognized the relation of his philosophical position to his inner self as a person, a Christian believer; and he is that, passionately so, throughout his work. The concluding line of his last book is simply *Amor vincit omnia!* It is evident not only in his thought but in his lifestyle. His letters and memos are signed again and again:

In Christian love,

Stu

I John 2:17

In offering to my former colleague an introduction to this *Festschrift* volume, then, I gladly do so

In Christian love,

Arthur F. Holmes
Wheaton College

---

[7]*Reconstruction*, p. 14.
[8]Ibid., p. 343.

Passionate Religion: Toward A Theory Of Epistemic Commitment For Theistic Belief

Mark S. McLeod
Westmont College

INTRODUCTION

The Bible commands Christians and Jews to love the Lord their God with all their hearts, souls, and minds. Some act on this command. When they do, how is the resulting deep religious commitment epistemically acceptable, given what many, theists and non-theists alike, see as the limited amount of evidence for theistic claims?

First, some preliminaries.

Belief

We can identify at least four senses of the term "belief," labeling them as follows: a) proposition, b) belief, c) acceptance, and d) commitment.

I mean by "proposition" what logicians sometimes mean, namely, that which is asserted by declarative utterances or that which is either true or false. The remaining three senses of "belief" stand in relation to this first sense. A proposition is that which is believed or accepted or that to which one is committed. Thus, belief, acceptance, and commitment are all propositional attitudes.

Alvin Plantinga's work helps to further explain these terms. After introducing the notion of a noetic structure (roughly, a set of propositions held by a person, along with certain epistemic relations that hold between him and these propositions), Plantinga lists what must be given in an account of a person's noetic structure.[1] He notes that one can distinguish between belief and acceptance. He writes:

> Consider a Christian beset by doubts. He has a hard time believing certain crucial Christian claims—perhaps the teaching that God was in Christ, reconciling the world to himself. Upon calling that belief to mind, he finds it cold, lifeless, without warmth or attractiveness. Nonetheless he is committed to this belief; it is his position; if you ask him what he thinks about it, he will unhesitatingly endorse it. He has, so to speak, thrown in his lot with it. Let us say that he *accepts* this proposition, even though when he is assailed by doubt, he may fail to *believe* it—at any rate explicitly—to any appreciable degree. His commitment to this proposition may be much stronger than his explicit and occurrent belief in it; so these two—that is, acceptance and belief—must be distinguished.[2]

Plantinga says no more about this distinction. Nevertheless, we can extract from his example that beliefs have warmth, attractiveness, and liveliness, whereas acceptances do not. Two things should be noted here. First, these characteristics are surely metaphorical. What exactly they come to, when stripped of the metaphor, is difficult to say. Perhaps these characteristics just are the fact that one believes rather than (merely) accepts. Second, whatever they come to, these characteristics surely have more to do with the psychology of the one holding the belief than they do with the propositions held.

---

[1]What follows is an incomplete list of Plantinga's suggestions. See the next note for further reference.

[2]Alvin Plantinga, "Reason and Belief in God," in *Faith and Rationality: Reason and Belief in God,* ed. Alvin Plantinga and Nicholas Wolterstorff (Notre Dame: University of Notre Dame Press, 1983), p. 37.

Plantinga also seems to suggest that one can doubt that *p* is true and yet accept it, whereas (employing the same notion of doubt) one cannot doubt *p* and yet believe *p*. One can accept some proposition, in spite of its lack of warmth, liveliness, and attractiveness. This may simply be an extension of the point above; perhaps doubt simply *is* the lack of these phenomenological features, just as belief is their presence.

What more can be said? Much, I think. Perhaps, however, enough has been said to provide an intuitive picture clear enough for the present discussion.

Plantinga also includes in his requirements for an account of a person's noetic structure both an index of degree of belief and an index of degree of acceptance. This brings us to the last sense of "belief," viz. commitment. Plantinga writes: "I believe both that $2 + 1 = 3$ and London, England, is north of Saskatoon, Saskatchewan; but I believe the former more resolutely than the latter."[3] Presumably he would say something similar about the index of degree of acceptance. At any rate, here we have what I wish to isolate as "commitment." We hold various propositions with various levels of firmness, whether they are held as beliefs or acceptances; one can be more or less committed to a proposition in terms of how deeply one believes it, as well as in terms of how deeply one accepts it. In short, one can be more or less deeply committed to a proposition; there are levels of commitment.

Furthermore, it appears that commitment of these two types (belief- and acceptance-commitment) can be at odds with one another. In his example, Plantinga suggests that the Christian's commitment to the proposition he accepts (but has a hard time believing) is greater than his occurrent belief in that proposition. While there is some unclarity in Plantinga's example, it seems to be the case that there are various levels of commitment to propositions, and this commitment is intimately related to belief and acceptance, even when belief and acceptance conflict.

Now it is certain that the demands of the Judaeo-Christian tradition involve passionate commitments. What kinds of epistemic constraint are such commitment under?

---

[3] Alvin Plantinga, "The Reformed Objection to Natural Theology," *Proceedings of the American Catholic Philosophical Association* 54 (1980):54.

The Justification Maxim

Let us say that one requirement of commitment is expressed by the Justification Maxim (JM). Roughly, the JM claims that no proposition ought to be given more (or less) commitment than its (epistemic) justification will bear. More formally, where "S" is some person, *p* is any proposition, and *PA* is any propositional attitude, let

JM = def. The commitment allotted *p* by S, via S's *PA*, ought to be commensurate with S's (epistemic) justification for *p*.

Note that the JM is a normative claim. How so? Again, some of Plantinga's claims can help us.

In describing a theory of rationality (foundationalism, in this case) Plantinga writes that

there is a right way and a wrong way with respect to belief. People have responsibilities, duties, and obligations with respect to their believings just as with respect to their (other) actions

and that

to be rational . . . is to exercise one's epistemic powers properly—to exercise them in such a way as to go contrary to none of the norms for such exercise.[4]

He further writes:

To be completely rational, as I am here using the term, is not to believe only what is true, or to believe all the logical consequences of what one believes, or to believe all necessary truths with equal firmness, or to be uninfluenced by emotion; it is, instead, to do the right thing with respect to one's believings.[5]

---

[4]Ibid., pp. 53, 54.
[5]Ibid., p. 55.

Plantinga's emphasis is clearly normative; there are certain obligations and duties which come into existence simply in virtue of having beliefs (and acceptances).[6] These normative claims on one's life are related less to believing certain kinds of things and more to one's actions *vis-à-vis* one's beliefs. I wish us to understand the JM in this way as well. One is required by normative epistemic demands to have one's believings and acceptings commensurate with one's epistemic justification for the corresponding propositions.

The Problem

Theistic belief is often, if not typically, taken by the mature believer as seriously as, or more seriously than, any other belief. This often means that when other beliefs conflict with theistic belief, the others lose out; the competing beliefs are modified or rejected in accordance with the demands of the theistic beliefs. This signals the extraordinary depth of the believer's commitment toward his theistic belief. My initial and central question is, then, how such deep commitment is justified *vis-à-vis* what many people, theist and non-theist alike, take to be the relative lack of evidence for theistic beliefs.

Here my concern is not that theistic propositions lack evidence altogether; it seems clear enough that they do not. My concern, that is, is not whether theists are rational in believing or accepting certain claims. That, it seems to me, is the burden and the success of recent work in religious epistemology, especially that done by Alvin Plantinga, Nicholas Wolterstorff, and William Alston.[7] Rather the problem is how to provide *sufficient* evidence for one's believings and acceptings in light of the very deep, heartfelt commitment the theistic believer often has toward these propositions.

---

[6]Elsewhere he discusses at length the nature of these normative considerations. See "Reason and Belief in God," especially pp. 29-39. In later work he moves away from the moral emphasis to a "standards" emphasis. See Alvin Plantinga, "Coherentism and the Evidentialist Objection to Belief in God," in *Rationality, Religious Belief, and Moral Commitment,* ed. Robert Audi and William J. Wainwright (Ithaca: Cornell University Press, 1986), p. 111.

[7]According to the work of these self-described "Reformed epistemologists," rationality, at least one kind of rationality, is what we might call "permissive rationality;" it allows us to believe but does not necessarily require or demand belief.

The Approach

Some of Plantinga's suggestions move us toward a solution to the problem of theistic commitment. Although I shall discuss some issues directly related to Plantinga's own claims, this is not my primary aim. I argue, in fact, that foundationalism is not the best epistemic theory by which to deal with the problem of commitment. Plantinga's work is very suggestive, however, and therefore makes an excellent place to begin. My suggestions are somewhat tentative and preliminary but I hope nevertheless helpful.

I first introduce Plantinga's criticism of classical foundationalism. Second, a challenge to his position is presented and a response developed. Out of this response comes a suggestion about fundamental assumptions of rationality and the role they play in our noetic structures. This, in turn, leads to a brief discussion of holism versus foundationalism and then to an application of the results of the discussion to the problem of religious attitudes and justification.

PLANTINGA'S CRITICISM OF CLASSICAL FOUNDATIONALISM

Plantinga believes that one of the fundamental challenges facing theistic belief is the evidentialist challenge. Extending its claims to include reference to acceptances as well as beliefs, evidentialism can be summarized as follows:

(1) There are obligations or standards of excellence with respect to belief and acceptance.

(2) It is either intellectually wrong or intellectually defective for anyone to believe or accept, upon insufficient evidence, any proposition requiring discursive justification.

(3) Since theistic beliefs require discursive justification, it is irrational or unreasonable to believe or accept theistic propositions in the absence of sufficient evidence or reasons.

In addition to (1) - (3), the evidentialist objector also holds:

(4) We have no evidence or at any rate not sufficient evidence for theistic propositions.

Note that evidentialism and the challenge to theistic belief that comes out of it both rely on the notion of discursive justification or evidence. They are thus rooted in classical foundationalism.

Classical Foundationalism

Classical foundationalism, according to Plantinga, claims that there are two types of beliefs, basic and non-basic. The former are non-discursive, the latter discursive. In addition, those beliefs can be either proper or not. Thus, a properly basic belief is one that is non-discursive but rational, that is, without epistemic fault *vis-à-vis* the demands placed on it by rationality. A properly non-basic belief, on the other hand, is one that is discursive and rational.

Here enters the evidentialist challenge. Theistic beliefs, if rational, cannot be non-discursive. For to be non-discursive and rational is to be properly basic, and theistic beliefs fail to meet the strong criteria for proper basicality proposed by the classical foundationalist. Thus we have the claim that theistic beliefs must be discursively justified, if at all. But are they justified in this manner? The failure of natural theology shows that they are not. Theistic beliefs fail to have discursive justification, so they fail to be rational. So goes the evidentialist challenge as it relies on classical foundationalism.

Two Criticisms

Plantinga's response to the evidentialist challenge, insofar as it is rooted in classical foundationalism, is two-fold. Let us call the first criticism the "self-referential incoherence criticism" and the second the "wide-spread belief criticism."

Self-referential Incoherence

Plantinga challenges the narrow understanding the classical foundationalist has of criteria for proper basicality. The classical criterion is as follows:

(5) "A proposition p is properly basic for a person S if and only if p is either self-evident to S, incorrigible for S, or evident to the senses for S."[8]

Now it is obvious that theistic beliefs are not properly basic if this is an accurate statement of the criterion. Beliefs about God are not self-evident, incorrigible, or evident to the senses.

But then neither is (5) properly basic by its own standards; (5) is not self-evident, incorrigible, or evident to the senses. In addition, (5) does not seem to follow discursively from any properly basic beliefs. Since all beliefs, if rational, must be either properly basic or properly non-basic, classical foundationalism is self-referentially incoherent.

Wide-spread Belief

Even were classical foundationalism not self-referentially incoherent, however, a second challenge would emerge. As the history of scepticism teaches, rather than being a steady rock on which to rest knowledge and rational belief, classical foundationalism has been the rock on which knowledge and rational belief founder. According to the sceptical tradition, classical foundationalism's criterion does not allow many of our ordinary beliefs to be justified. That Susan is in pain, or that there is a tree in front of us, are claims which are not properly basic according to (5). Yet we have no argument for these beliefs or their kind; we can give no discursive account of them vis-à-vis the requirements of classical foundationalism. They are thus not properly non-basic either, and scepticism is at the door. How can classical foundationalism remain a viable theory when many of our wide-spread beliefs cannot be justified in light of its demands? For Plantinga, it is not viable and ought to be rejected.

---

[8]Plantinga, "Reason and Belief in God," p. 59.

Of course, if classical foundationalism is not viable, then neither is evidentialism insofar as it grows out of classical foundationalism. Thus, the evidentialist challenge to theistic belief is not viable either. However, Plantinga opens the door to another theory of rationality that does not, he thinks, rule out the proper basicality of our wide-spread beliefs or of theistic beliefs.

DISCOVERING CRITERIA FOR PROPER BASICALITY

Since the classical criterion for proper basicality has been rejected as too narrow, whatever replacement is suggested should be broad enough to allow our wide-spread beliefs to be rational. In particular, Plantinga mentions beliefs about other minds, beliefs about the external world, and beliefs about the past. I do not think Plantinga would be against adding to this list beliefs about how we discover things about the world, specifically the principles of induction, deduction, the scientific method, and the like. However, I see no easy way to capture such principles. Let us just say that those principles which we typically use to advance our knowledge ought not to be ruled out by the replacement criterion.

With these restrictions on what we will take as an acceptable criterion, how does Plantinga suggest we discover a criterion for proper basicality?

Plantinga's Approach

Plantinga writes that

The proper way to arrive at such a criterion is, broadly speaking, *inductive*. We must assemble examples of beliefs and conditions such that the former are obviously properly basic in the latter, and examples of beliefs and conditions such that the former are not properly basic in the latter. We must then frame hypotheses as to the necessary and sufficient conditions of proper basicality and test these hypotheses by reference to those examples.[9]

Thus,

---

[9]Alvin Plantinga, "Is Belief in God Properly Basic?" *Noûs* 15 (1981):50.

Criteria for proper basicality must be reached from below rather than above; they should not be presented as *ex cathedra*, but argued to and tested by a relevant set of examples. But there is no reason to assume, in advance, that everyone will agree on the examples. The Christian will of course suppose that belief in God is entirely proper and rational; if he doesn't accept this belief on the basis of other propositions, he will conclude that it is basic for him and quite properly so. Followers of Bertrand Russell and Madelyn Murray O'Hare may disagree, but how is that relevant? Must my criteria, or those of the Christian community, conform to their examples? Surely not. The Christian community is responsible to its set of examples, not to theirs.[10]

Thus we should use an inductive procedure to discover a criterion for proper basicality. Can this approach be successful in producing the results Plantinga desires?

A Challenge

The classical foundationalist might suggest in reply that since Plantinga's suggested procedure is person- or community-relative, it may be possible to find a group of classical foundationalists who hold (5) as the criterion for proper basicality *and* who find (5) to be self-evident. This is possible on Plantinga's own grounds, they say, for Plantinga suggests elsewhere that "self-evidence" is a person-relative notion.[11]

Suppose, then, that the classical foundationalists do some field work, finding a group of epistemologists[12] who have done Plantinga's suggested inductive procedure. Furthermore, suppose this group find (5) to be self-evident. For these epistemologists,

---

[10]Ibid.

[11]See Alvin Plantinga, "Is Belief in God Rational?" *Rationality and Religious Belief*, ed C.F. Delaney (Notre Dame: University of Notre Dame Press, 1979), where Plantinga discusses self-evidence at length. In a delightful story by George Mavrodes in the same volume, Mavrodes pokes fun at the notion of self-evidence as described by Plantinga. In the story, a proof for God's existence begins with the self-evident premise that Jesus Christ rose from the dead!

[12]Living, no doubt, in relative obscurity somewhere between Grand Rapids and Ann Arbor, Michigan, in other words, between the ostensible center of Plantinga's Reformed epistemology and the University of Michigan, where Mavrodes teaches!

(call them the "entrenched classical foundationalists" or ECF), since (5) is self-evident, the self-referential criticism fails.

The Reply

Plantinga can retort as follows. First, by suggesting that self-evidence is person-relative, he does not mean that just anything can be taken to be self-evident. Generally, self-evident propositions are person-relative only in the sense that as one's knowledge of a field grows, one's grasp of the truths in that field becomes deeper. For example, some mathematical proposition which was self-evident for Einstein is not for me. It might *become* self-evident for me if I study enough mathematics, but it is not right now. But it is unlikely that one's knowledge of epistemology will ever help one come to grasp self-evidently a proposition as controversial as (5). Unlike some mathematical propositions, even if (5) is explained to me I will never self-evidently "see" it. On this basis Plantinga might ask the members of the ECF if they *really* find (5) self-evident or if they are only digging deep to uncover something that will protect their favorite theory.

Second, and more importantly, Plantinga can fall back on the wide-spread belief criticism. Even if (5) truly does seem self-evident to members of the ECF, according to classical foundationalism the principle by which it was supposedly discovered to be a criterion for proper basicality must still be justified. But besides using inductive procedures to discover the criterion for proper basicality, the members of the ECF presumably use inductive procedures for other things. Yet (5) seems to rule out their legitimate use. This, of course, has been a sceptical thorn in the classical foundationalist's flesh for centuries.

The ECF might suggest that inductive principles are themselves self-evident, but this move seems to open the foundations to just about anything's being self-evident. Such a move would play into Plantinga's hands, for if that is what one means by self-evidence, why not take theistic beliefs to be self-evident (and thus properly basic) as well?

As an alternative, the ECF may suggest that inductive principles ought to be understood as part of a heuristic meta-epistemological framework. By definition, however, this is ruled out. Foundationalism requires that all rational beliefs be either properly basic or non-basic. Belief in the principles of induction cannot be outside one's noetic structure. How, then, are inductive principles to be justified?

Inductive Principles and Criteria for Proper Basicality

Does Plantinga's modified foundationalism fare any better on this issue? I believe the answer is affirmative. Caution is needed, however, for there is one thing we learn from the wide-spread belief criticism: the criteria for properly basic beliefs should not be overly strong.

It is easy enough to desire overly strong criteria. Plantinga seems to do this himself in his response to the "Great Pumpkin objection." The objection is this:

If belief in God is properly basic, why can't just any belief be properly basic? Couldn't we say the same about any bizarre aberration we can think of? What about voodoo or astrology? What about the belief that the Great Pumpkin returns every Halloween? Could I properly take *that* as basic? . . . If we say that belief in God is properly basic, won't we be committed to holding that just anything, or nearly anything, can properly be taken as basic, thus throwing wide the gates to irrationalism and superstition?[13]

In his response, Plantinga makes it clear that not just any belief can be properly basic but that a properly basic belief, although lacking discursive evidence, does not lack grounding. Thus, some beliefs are not properly basic because they lack grounding. Further, Plantinga claims that arriving at the criterion for proper basicality leads to charging belief in the Great Pumpkin with irrationality. But why should the Great Pumpkinite accept this? Admittedly, belief in the Great Pumpkin is not something I take to be rational, but what if we come upon some tribe that believes it is? Suppose this tribe has read Plantinga, followed his inductive procedure, and takes Great Pumpkin belief as properly basic? Suppose they even specify their criterion for proper basicality and it does not lead to any incoherence? What is Plantinga to say?

Perhaps Plantinga's desire to rule out Great Pumpkin belief is motivated by the fact that we do not have any natural inclination to believe in the Great Pumpkin, whereas

---

[13]Plantinga, "The Reformed Objection to Natural Theology," p. 58.

we do have a natural inclination to believe in God. Nevertheless, Plantinga *qua* theist would surely admit the rationality of Great Pumpkin belief insofar as such belief actually resembles theistic belief. But isn't this just to say that the force of Plantinga's response is derived from the oddity of the example he chooses? Had he chosen Buddhism or Hinduism, perhaps the rejection of the objection would not seem to follow quite so quickly.

How would it be possible, once the inductive procedure is completed, for Great Pumpkin belief to be rejected as irrational? First, if no one ever has Great Pumpkin experiences and simply choses arbitrarily to believe in the Great Pumpkin, no such belief is rational. It is not grounded. Second, if one does have Great Pumpkin experiences to ground such belief and Plantinga still rejects the belief as irrational, he must mean that *no* Great Pumpkinite's belief is rational. He must, in other words, have some independent reason for rejecting Great Pumpkin belief, viz., it fails to meet *Plantinga's* criterion. He must hold that the criteria for proper basicality are quite strong; so strong as not to be person-relative. Plantinga seems to think this way, at least part of the time; if one inductively arrives at P as the criterion for proper basicality and P rules out Great Pumpkin belief, then no one's belief in the Great Pumpkin could be rational. But, *pace* Plantinga, what if the Great Pumpkinite takes his belief to be properly basic and thus arrives at a different criterion? Plantinga's response is inconsistent with his inductive procedure and its potential results. To be consistent, he must allow for such a potentiality. The Great Pumpkin objection, understood as the demand for a very liberal openness to what *might* count as properly basic, stands against his theory and thus Plantinga is committed to a weaker sense of rationality than some of his comments would indicate.

Since Plantinga himself struggles with the status of criteria for proper basicality, one wonders about the proper way to understand them. We can say at least two things. First, any criterion must itself be rationally justified. Second, inductive procedures can justify some criteria. This latter point entails that the proposition expressing a criterion will be non-basic, since the proposition (or rather its belief or acceptance) will be based on others. The principles of induction, on the other hand, can be either basic or non-basic. Either way, the criterion must not be overly strong or the grounding of the principles of induction becomes impossible. If the principles are to be properly basic, the criteria cannot rule them out. If they are to be non-basic, there must be some properly basic belief (or set of beliefs) to justify the principles of induction that is not itself ruled out by the criteria. For our purposes, given a sufficiently weak criterion, the principles of induction can be properly basic. Let me provide a sketch to show how.

Suppose we set out to discover which of our beliefs are properly basic. We decide that if anything is properly basic, beliefs A, B, C, and the principles of induction are. Of course, at this time we do not know the criterion for proper basicality. Intuitively, however, we take these beliefs as basic and properly so. We discover inductively that these beliefs all share property P. P is thus the criterion for proper basicality. P can be based on at least one other belief, specifically, one of the principles of induction. Thus, P is non-basic, yet functions as a criterion for A, B, C, and the principles of induction. Induction thus legitimately justifies P. The principles of induction, on the other hand, need not be discursively justified but are grounded, since they fall under the criterion discovered by the inductive approach.

WIDESPREAD BELIEFS AS
FUNDAMENTAL ASSUMPTIONS OF RATIONALITY

The above suggestions leave open the possibility of accounting for our widespread belief in the principles of induction. In fact, on the account sketched above these principles play an important role in discovering the replacement criterion for proper basicality and yet do not lead to the kind of self-referential incoherence found in classical foundationalism.

But what about other widespread beliefs such as beliefs about other persons, the external world, or the past? Do these fare as well? I believe they do, but we have not the space to consider them individually. Instead I wish to consider why these so-called widespread beliefs are important to rationality.

A Freshman Fallacy

It would be a mistake to think that the importance of these widespread beliefs for rationality lies in the fact that most everyone takes them to be true. First of all, it clearly does not follow from the fact that most people hold (versions of) the widespread beliefs that the beliefs are indeed true. This is a variation of that infamous freshman fallacy of the band-wagon. But even if they were all true, their truth does not necessarily make them rational. What does?

World-ordering Power

Consider these propositions: "There are other people alive," "there are real trees (or rocks, or mountains, or the like)," and "I remember yesterday's events accurately." Such propositions, whether held as beliefs or acceptances, play central roles in our lives. One cannot imagine, at least with any seriousness, living life without them (or at least their near relatives). Why do we take them so seriously? Why do we take them as a necessary starting point for any theory of rationality? Simply stated, I believe they have the ability to greatly arrange and order our other beliefs and acceptances.

There appears to be a hierarchy of beliefs and acceptances in our noetic structures. Some we are willing to give up quite quickly; others we are not. What I have been calling "widespread beliefs" fall into the latter category. Another notion from Plantinga's work can help us explore the importance of this observation. He claims that in describing one's noetic structure one will have to include an index of *depth of ingression*. He writes:

> Some of my beliefs are, we might say, on the periphery of my noetic structure.
> I accept them, and may even accept them quite firmly, but if I were to give them
> up, not much else in my noetic structure would have to change. I believe there
> are some large boulders on the top of the Grand Teton. If I come to give up this
> belief, however, . . . that change wouldn't have extensive reverberations
> throughout the rest of my noetic structure; it could be accommodated with
> minimal alteration elsewhere. So its depth of ingression into my noetic structure
> isn't great. On the other hand, if I were to come to believe that there simply is
> no such thing as the Grand Teton, or no such thing as the state of Wyoming,
> that would have much greater reverberations. And if, per impossible, I were to
> come to think there hadn't been much of a past . . . or that there weren't any
> other persons, that would have even greater reverberations; these beliefs of
> mine have great depth of ingression into my noetic structure.[14]

---

[14]Ibid., p. 55.

To give up some beliefs would radically alter one's noetic structure. The connections between beliefs can be enormous in number and complicated in kind. I suggest that the reason the so-called "widespread beliefs" are so important to rationality is that they have, to borrow Plantinga's phrase, the greatest depth of ingression. Perhaps more intuitive terminology would be helpful here. Let us say that such beliefs have the greatest world-ordering power.

Before moving on, it is important to clarify exactly which beliefs or acceptances have the status of being widespread, as well as the relationships between the notion of world-ordering power and notions such as level of commitment, belief, and acceptance.

Identifying Widespread Beliefs

Obviously we cannot simply identify "widespread" beliefs as person-specific beliefs. For example,

(a) I am writing at a brown desk

is not widespread. Since you are reading, rather than writing, (a) is not one of your current beliefs. Neither, in all likelihood, is (a) a belief many people have right now.

It is also not the case that

(b) there is an external world

is widely held in the sense that most people now *believe* it. Most non-philosophers have not even thought about it, let alone believe it! In fact, it is not belief *qua* propositional attitude which is important at all. Instead we should consider beliefs *qua* propositions.

But it is not *idiosyncratic* propositions that are truly central either. Rather it is the *kind* of proposition that is important. Here the "kind" is picked out by the various contents of beliefs; there are beliefs that are about physical objects, others that are about other persons, still others about the past, and so forth. It is certain kinds of proposition that are widespreadly held, rather than any idiosyncratic proposition. Everyone holds these kinds of propositions: physical-object propositions, other-mind propositions, and so forth. And while we are willing to admit that we can be wrong about some individual members of the various kinds, we are not typically willing to admit that we can be wrong about the entire kind.

So the terminology "widespread belief" is misleading in two ways. What is important for our discussion is not beliefs *qua* propositional attitude. Nor is it belief *qua* idiosyncratic proposition. What is important is rather that certain *assumptions* are made by every person with ordinary beliefs. It is here, I believe, that the distinction between beliefs and acceptances becomes important. As noted, most people do not explicitly believe propositions such as "There is an external world," or "There are other minds" and the like. I have little doubt, however, that upon inquiry most people would admit that they at least accept such propositions as background assumptions. These propositions are immediately entailed by the ordinary kinds of propositions that we all hold. Even though most people do not explicitly believe them (not ever having really thought about them), they do believe propositions that fall into the kinds "external-world propositions," "other-mind propositions," and so forth. Our acceptance or assumption of propositions such as "There is an external world" and "There are other minds" simply express our commitment to our ordinary beliefs being (generally) rational.

These acceptances are greatly world-ordering. They are parts of the complex of speech and action (to which many philosophers have called attention, from Aristotle to Moore and Wittgenstein) that go into making up our shared lives together. One cannot successfully ignore or question these acceptances; questioning comes to an end. These acceptances are so deeply embedded in our noetic structures and our human culture that we simply cannot shake them off. Since we must start somewhere in giving an account of rationality, we might just as well begin with the paradigm cases that seem to be necessary for human communication and culture. These acceptances, in a way, are what *make* us rational.

If I am right about this, then the concerns of Plantinga's "widespread belief criticism" appear to be concerns about giving an account of certain acceptances that all rational persons have. We all accept certain propositions about reality. Any theory of rationality that does not explain them is to be rejected on the grounds that it overlooks our fundamental rationality.

World-ordering Power, Commitment,
and Fundamental Assumptions of Rationality

In light of all this, let what I have been calling a "widespread belief" now be referred to as a "fundamental assumption of rationality" or a FAR. We can turn now to give an account of how FARs are related to commitment and world-ordering power.

First, we need a more formal account of world-ordering power (WP). Thus,

WP=$_{def}$. The ability of a (change in) belief in, or acceptance of, a (given) proposition to adjust other beliefs or acceptances in S's noetic structure.

All beliefs and acceptances have the power to make us adjust our noetic structures. When we take on a new belief, we make other changes as well. When we lose an acceptance, we make other adjustments to go with the loss. What I wish to propose for consideration is that WP is connected to a principle of rationality, namely, the JM.

The JM demands that no proposition be held with greater commitment than that permitted by its justification. Taking commitment to be the level of (un)willingness to give up one's propositional attitude toward a proposition, then one must find some principle that connects one's commitment with one's justification for the proposition. I suggest that one possibility for linking commitment to epistemic justification is to make commitment a function of WP. Let's call this the Principle of Commitment (PC). It says this:

PC=$_{def}$. S's (belief- or acceptance-) commitment to a proposition p ought to be commensurate with the world-ordering power of p for S.

Accordingly, the more world-ordering power a belief or acceptance has, the more epistemic justification it has. Thus those beliefs or acceptances that have the least WP are those to which we should be least committed, while those with the greatest WP ought to be those with the greatest commitment.[15] This raises the obvious question, what does the WP of a belief or acceptance have to do with its epistemic justification?

There are a variety of answers that could be given here. I will limit my discussion to two, rejecting the first. Return to the sketch above where Plantinga's inductive procedure was used to discover a criterion for proper basicality while allowing the wide-spread belief in induction to be rational. There it was suggested that some property P is shared by all the beliefs we intuitively take to be properly basic. Thus P is the criterion for proper basicality. My initial answer linking WP to justification is simply that P may be the WP of the properly basic beliefs in question; $A, B, C,$ and the principles of induction all share the same level of WP. What level? It seems that it would have to be the greatest level of WP for S, for according to foundationalism, properly basic beliefs are to play a special role in one's noetic structure.

Traditionally, foundationalists thought that one's properly basic beliefs were beliefs that were without epistemic fault; in particular they were thought to carry a guarantee of truth. Of course, more recent versions of foundationalism have given up the high goal of truth-guarantee. Nevertheless, the assumption that basic beliefs play a special role remains. Plantinga, for example, writes:

> From the foundationalist point of view not just any kind of belief can be found in the foundations of a rational noetic structure; a belief to be properly basic (that is, basic in a rational noetic structure) must meet certain conditions. It must be capable of functioning foundationally, capable of bearing its share of the weight of the whole noetic structure.[16]

What is it for a belief to be capable of functioning foundationally, to be able to bear its share of the weight? Well, on the classical model of foundationalism, it was to be self-evident, incorrigible, or evident to the senses. But as we have seen, these suggestions are problematic *vis-à-vis* the demands of classical foundationalism itself, as well as in giving an account the FAR.

---

[15]This is contrary to the above quotation from Plantinga where he indicates that a belief can be firmly held (deeply committed) but be on the periphery of one's noetic structure (not greatly world-ordering).

[16]Plantinga, "Reason and Belief in God," p. 55.

One suggestion is that to be foundational, and properly so, is to have the greatest level of WP. One can see right away, however, that this suggestion is problematical. One of the most obvious difficulties is that beliefs such as "Susan is in pain" and "There is a tree over there" (examples of beliefs which are obviously properly basic in the right conditions) do not have the greatest level of WP. One can give up one of these idiosyncratic propositions without making much change in one's noetic structure at all. Perhaps one is hallucinating, or perhaps Susan is feigning pain for sympathy.

Recall that the propositions that I identified earlier as being of the most significance were not idiosyncratic propositions but rather the FAR. On the account given to this point, only the FAR turn out to have the greatest WP, while other cases of properly basic beliefs (such as "Susan is in pain") do not. It seems clear enough, then, that aligning WP with the criterion for proper basicalilty as a means to account for commitment will not do.

Since the FAR are the propositions that have the greatest WP, it is important to provide a theory of rational noetic structures that takes this into account. My second answer linking WP to justification is that the WP of a proposition within a noetic structure is one of a number of coherence-relations which hold among one's beliefs and acceptances. With this suggestion we leave a foundationalist account of rational noetic structures and move to holism.

Holism vs. Foundationalism

I have heard it said that foundationalism is the most attractive position *vis-à-vis* epistemic considerations for the theist. One reason for this suggestion is the supposedly strong warrant for properly basic beliefs. When a basic belief is grounded, according to foundationalism, there is a tie onto the independently existing world; the belief is justified independently of the system of beliefs. This independent tie is often associated with a realist understanding, both in metaphysics and epistemology, a view attractive to theists who typically believe that God created the world and that the world therefore exists independently of human thought about it. But if God is who the theist thinks He is, why could one not know about God in the independent way foundationalism suggests? Thus the attractiveness of foundationalism.

With holism, however, one has no "tie" to the independent world. Holist models of epistemic justification tend to give little or minimal justification for a given belief. Rather, a belief is only justified within a given noetic structure. In fact, it is the *structure* that is justified rather than individual propositions. The system-relativity of holism and the lack of tie to the supposedly independently existing world are two reasons for the theist to balk at holism.

Nevertheless, realism in metaphysics may have little to do with epistemology. Some things may be real, and independently so, and yet our access to them be limited. We may be, as finite humans, trapped within our systems of beliefs. They may not reflect reality. But if giving a holist account is the best we can do, so be it. Being a theist does not clearly, or even naturally, lead to being a foundationalist.

Furthermore, I believe the present discussion gives some reason to move to holism. Foundationalism, even Plantinga's relatively weak version, does not have much potential for providing an account of passionate commitment or, for that matter, levels of commitment that match our experience of how religious people act *vis-à-vis* their religious beliefs. The account of the criterion for proper basicality that Plantinga provides (with or without the modification I suggested above) may give us non-discursive warrant for single, individual beliefs such as "I see a tree" but it does little to account for the FAR. What is really important are not Plantinga's widespread beliefs understood as individual beliefs, but the FAR which underlie them. These propositions, and our attitudes toward them, are what are truly central for rationality. A holist account of rationality that will provide a means of accounting for levels of commitment will have to include some principle of rationality that connects commitment to something like WP. Can this be done? I believe so, but the detail will have to await a longer work.

THE JM AND THEISTIC BELIEF

I have suggested that the JM demands commitment commensurate with epistemic justification and that one potential principle that might provide a link between the two is the PC. By way of conclusion I wish to make some observations about religious belief and its WP.

I have said that the FAR are not, in the typical case, beliefs but rather that they are closer to acceptances. Most people do not explicitly believe that there is an external world, or that there are other minds, and so forth. They simply accept (often unconsciously) such propositions; the propositions are fundamental assumptions of rationality. Nevertheless, the commitment which people have toward these propositions is great indeed, a fact illustrated by the difficulties teachers of philosophy have in convincing their students that the problem of the external world is a real problem! These assumptions are deeply embedded.

If this is true, then it may appear that my suggestions will not apply to religion and that the goal set for the paper will not be met. Theism, after all, involves beliefs. Christianity in particular calls for belief; one is to "believe on the Lord Jesus Christ" to be saved. But if belief is fundamental to theism, and yet it is the FAR *qua* acceptances that have the greatest WP, then how is it that radical, heartfelt theistic commitment can be justified *vis-à-vis* the JM and the argument of this essay?

This question can be more easily handled if broken down into two questions. First, does religion involve fundamental assumptions of rationality?

The theist, and in particular the Christian theist, will respond from within his or her system of belief. The answer, given the truth of Christianity, is that yes, theistic beliefs and acceptances are part and parcel with what it is to be rational. What rational person would refuse the call and demands of God, the Creator, on his or her life? Now the Christian may not be so bold as to suggest that someone is irrational in not being a Christian, but it seems quite consistent to say that one is not fully rational if one lacks Christian faith.

The second question is this. The FAR are closer to acceptances than they (typically) are to beliefs. But theistic faith involves belief, not mere acceptance. How can theistic belief then involve the great level of world-ordering power that the other FAR do? A complete answer to this question would require much more space than we have here. Perhaps the following will suffice.

It is often noted that the nature of theistic belief is far more complicated than our more ordinary beliefs in propositions. Theistic belief is much closer to trusting one's spouse or best friend than it is to merely believing that there is a tree in the front yard. But theistic faith is complicated in another way as well. It functions, at least for the mature believer, as a screen through which other competitors for belief and acceptance are sifted.[17] I think these two points are intimately connected. The following analogy will aim our thinking in the right direction.

I believe in my wife, much in the same way as I believe in God. I love her, I react to her wants and desires, I listen to her, and so forth. I do likewise with God. I love Him, I move on (what I take to be) His wants and desires, I listen to Him, and so forth. But with my wife I also evaluate my actions and thoughts through her concerns. This is not always conscious. Neither is it always done with passionate *belief*. There are things, for example, that I simply *accept* about my wife, and that I do not necessarily believe, at least occurrently. I accept that she will act in certain ways toward me, I accept that her character will be more or less consistent over a period of time, and so forth.

Now it seems to me that I have not always accepted these things. Prior to my having come to accept them, I believed them. It was much more important for me, in the relative immaturity of our early relationship, to have these things before my mind's eye as things to which I was attracted, as things that I found warm. But it was when I moved from explicitly believing these things to accepting them that real maturity in my marriage became possible. It was by my very *acceptance* of them that I began to recognize my deep commitment to them and, by extension, to her. (This is not, of course, to say that I never have the propositional attitude of belief toward these things. It is only to say that often I do not and that the lack of belief does not adversely affect the good relationship I have with my wife.)

Likewise with belief in God. The mature believer accepts certain things about God, His nature, His character, and so forth. He or she need not believe them in the explicit, conscious sense to which we have made reference. This is why in Plantinga's example of the doubting Christian, the doubter has not lost his faith. He accepts the problematic proposition; he has thrown in his lot with it.

There is, in short, an aspect of acceptance that was over-looked in the earlier description of the distinctions between belief and acceptance. Some might think of acceptance as a less important propositional attitude than belief. This, I think, is not the case, at least not for all acceptances. That there is a material world, that there are other persons, that we have some principles by which knowledge can advance, are

---

[17]Nicholas Wolterstorff develops this theme in some detail in *Reason Within the Bounds of Religion* (Grand Rapids, MI: Wm. B. Eerdmans, 1976).

acceptances of which we are largely not conscious; our propositional attitude toward them is not explicit as belief is. Yet we do not treat them lightly *when they are challenged.* The religious believer still accepts, although doubts, that God was in Christ reconciling the world to Himself. Belief may come and go; it waxes and wanes with the times. But acceptance is something we do more out of a sense of necessity—the necessity of making sense of our experience of reality.

Religious faith does involve acceptances and thus propositions involved in such faith can be members of the FAR. As such, deep commitment given to theistic propositions is justified, at least potentially, by the great level of world-ordering power the propositions have for theists.

The Justification Of Doctrinal Beliefs

W. Jay Wood

Wheaton College

It is unlikely in today's philosophical arena that the Christian philosopher who espouses minimal theism will be assailed by charges of intellectual wrongdoing, epistemic impropriety, or related accusations. But can Christians claim similar confidence in the justifiability of their doctrinal beliefs? Here I refer to what are commonly called the "mysteries of the faith": beliefs such as "Jesus Christ is God Incarnate," "There will be a general resurrection of the dead," and "God is triune." How do Christians justify such beliefs? Are they properly basic? Are they supported through argumentation? The concern of this paper is the epistemic status of doctrinal beliefs. Granted that Christians are justified in believing that God exists, it remains an open question whether they are entitled to their distinctive doctrinal beliefs.[1]

In this paper I wish to accomplish two things. First, to highlight quickly a few of the important differences between two contrasting strategies for justifying doctrinal

---

[1]Unless otherwise stated, I use the term "justification" to mean permissive justification. That is, one is rational in believing P if one has done one's epistemic best and is innocent of any intellectual improprieties. This should be contrasted with the stronger notion of justification which requires that a belief possess positive epistemic status for a person. It is justification as "positive epistemic status" that transmutes true belief into knowledge.

beliefs: that of evidentialists like John Locke and Stuart Hackett on the one hand, and that of the Reformed epistemologists on the other. Secondly, and more importantly, to articulate and assess the position that our doctrinal beliefs are properly basic.

LOCKE'S EVIDENTIALIST CASE
FOR DOCTRINAL BELIEFS

Locke's strategy for justifying doctrinal beliefs, like that of most seventeenth and eighteenth century apologists, takes an evidential turn. While the mysteries of the faith are not demonstrable, that does not mean that our justifiably believing them is gratuitous. They, like any other belief to which we are entitled, must be reasonable; that is, supported by evidence. "Faith is nothing but a firm assent of the mind: which if it be regulated, as is our duty, cannot be afforded to anything but upon good reason: and so cannot be opposite to it."[2]

The evidence Locke cites in support of doctrinal beliefs is indirect. It is not the doctrinal beliefs themselves which receive the support of reason; rather it is the belief that the doctrines in question have been revealed by God. "Whatever God hath revealed is certainly true; no doubt can be made of it. But whether it be a divine revelation or not, reason must judge . . ." (*Essay*, Bk. IV, 18, 10). It is important to stress the primacy of reason in determining the authenticity of a revelation claim.

> God when he makes the prophet does not unmake the man. He leaves all his faculties in their natural state, to enable him to judge of his inspirations whether they be of divine original or not. If he would have us assent to the truth of any proposition, he either evidences that truth by the usual methods of natural reason, or else makes it known to us by his authority, and convinces us that it is from him, by some marks which reason cannot be mistaken in (*Essay*, Bk. IV, 19, 14).

---

[2]John Locke, *An Essay Concerning Human Understanding* (New York, 1959), Bk.IV, 17, 24, p. 413. For convenience's sake, I will hereafter document quotations from Locke's work parenthetically within the body of the text.

What are the marks by which we know that some doctrine proposed for belief is from God? Locke cites three, the last being of greatest importance. (1) The content of the revelation must not contravene the self-evident principles of reason or anything derivative therefrom (*Essay*, Bk. IV, 18, 5). (2) No mission can be looked upon as divine, says Locke, that is inconsistent with natural religion, derogates from the honor of the one true God, or violates the rules of morality (*Essay*, Bk. IV, 18, 5). (3) When originally given, the revelation must be accompanied by a divine sign such as a miracle or prophecy, both of which demonstrate the intimate acquaintance and good favor of God. Two quotations, the first from *The Reasonableness of Christianity*, and the second from *A Discourse on Miracles* illustrate this last point:

> The evidence of our Saviour's mission from God is so great, in the multitude of miracles he did, before all sorts of people, that what he delivered cannot but be received as the oracles of God, and unquestioned verity. For the miracles he did were so ordered by the divine providence and wisdom, that they were never, nor could be denied by any enemies or opposers of Christianity.[3]

> ... He who comes with a message from God to be delivered to the world cannot be refused belief if he vouches his mission by a miracle, because his credentials have a right to it. For every rational thinking man must conclude as Nicodemus did, "we know that thou art a teacher come from God, for no man can do these signs which thou doest, except God be with him."[4]

There are difficulties too numerous to mention in Locke's efforts to justify doctrinal beliefs. I shall mention only two, since they bear on the development of the rest of the paper. First of all, the connection between our witnessing a miracle and our accepting as true the teaching of the prophet who performed it is tenuous at best. An obvious difficulty is that there is no logical connection between the powers and wonders displayed by a prophet and the truth of his teachings. The performance of a miracle is

---

[3] John Locke, *The Reasonableness of Christianity* with *A Discourse on Miracles* and part of *A Third Letter Concerning Toleration*, ed. I.T. Ramsey (Stanford: Stanford Univesity Press, 1958), p. 57.

[4] Ibid., p. 82.

neither a necessary nor a sufficient condition of the truthfulness of a revelation claim. Moreover, it is not clear that astounding deeds cannot be wrought by malevolent beings whose purpose is to deceive us.

A second and more serious problem surrounds the task of establishing the historical credentials for miracle claims. Since most of us are neither the beneficiaries of nor the witnesses to miraculous states of affairs, we depend on testimony and historical documents for our knowledge of them. Why is this problematic? First of all, Locke believes that the level of assent due any belief grounded in testimony or the probabilistic reasoning of the historical sciences is less than certain. Yet we are obliged by our religion to embrace its doctrines with all our heart, mind, and strength. Thus, there is an incongruity between the quality of evidence supporting the occurrence of miracles and the level of assent due the beliefs they undergird. Secondly, the ardors of historical scholarship surpass the capabilities of most people. The ability to assess the reliability of oral tradition, familiarity with archaeology, and a working understanding of the methods of historical research and criticism are skills possessed mostly by experts.[5]

While these difficulties may not be insuperable, I doubt that it will be contested that "the man in the pew" is largely unaware of the evidences supporting his religion and even less aware of the arguments proposed to discredit it. The question lingers, then, whether the ordinary believer's justification hinges on his having gone through the intellectual machinations of the apologist or historian. Such requirements are excessively burdensome; it seems epistemologically suspect to claim that my justifiably believing in the Trinity depends on my having amassed sufficient evidence. But are such requirements necessary? A merit of Reformed epistemology is not only that it takes belief in God as basic but holds that our doctrines can be justifiably believed independently of argumentative support. So let us turn to this alternative strategy for justifying doctrinal beliefs.

---

[5]Those familiar with Stuart Hackett's *The Reconstruction of the Christian Revelation Claim* will recognize a certain kinship between it and the concerns of Locke. Like Locke, Hackett displays a robust confidence in the ability of reason to provide a rational foundation for the Christian revelation claim. But those interested in following Hackett's intellectually rigorous defense of the Christian worldview must traverse much difficult theological and philosophical terrain. For Hackett, the road to justified Christian belief involves proving the existence of God, establishing the historical credentials for Christ's resurrection, demonstrating the logical coherence of the Trinity, and defending the revelatory status of the Bible.

REFORMED EPISTEMOLOGY AND EVIDENTIALISM

Locke's preoccupation with amassing sufficient evidence for beliefs is symptomatic of his commitment to the following two philosophical theses: (1) evidentialism: the thesis that we ought to proportion our beliefs to the evidence, and (2) foundationalism: a broader construal of the nature of knowledge. Of late, both these have come under considerable attack by Reformed epistemologists. The upshot of their criticisms of Locke and others is that belief in God is not the sort of belief for which evidence is needed. It is "properly basic"; reasonably believed, but not on the basis of any other beliefs which serve as its evidence. In this section I would like briefly to recapitulate the main components of the Reformed epistemologist's attack on evidentialism in order to determine what value such an approach has for doctrinal beliefs. Specifically, I would like to examine the suggestion of some Reformed thinkers that our doctrinal beliefs are properly basic. That is to say, in the same way in which the belief that "God exists" may be justifiably held without the support of other beliefs, so, too, may the truths of faith be held.

According to Plantinga, the total intellectual superstructure within which evidentialism rests is that of classical foundationalism.[6]

The rudiments of classical foundationalism are well known and much discussed. It is a famous rational reconstruction of human knowledge describing the logical priority and interrelationships that obtain in our noetic structure. It is also a normative thesis concerning the proper ordering of one's cognitive life. Briefly, foundationalism has three salient features; basic beliefs, non-basic beliefs, and the interrelations between the two. Basic beliefs are justifiably held in the absence of any argumentative support. A properly basic belief is one which is either self-evident (intuitively obvious to reason), incorrigible, or evident to the senses. These beliefs in turn provide the warrant for non-basic beliefs. Non-basic beliefs are either logically derivable from or probable with respect to what is basic. Hence, Locke held that God's existence, while not basic, was nonetheless certain insofar as it is derivable by self-evident inferences from self-evidently true basic beliefs.

---

[6]See Plantinga's essay "Reason and Belief in God," in *Faith and Rationality*, ed. N. Wolterstorff and A. Plantinga (Notre Dame: University of Notre Dame Press, 1983).

Plantinga's main thrust against evidentialism and the classical foundationalist epistemology that undergirds it is to question the traditional criteria for proper basicality. They are problematic on two counts. First, these criteria fail to countenance obvious cases of belief we accept as basic, such as our beliefs in other minds and the external world. A second, and more ignominious, failing of classical foundationalism is that its demand that basic beliefs be self-evident, evident to the senses, or incorrigible is self-referentially inconsistent. For this claim neither satisfies the very conditions it lays down, nor is it derivable from more basic beliefs that do satisfy the criteria.

The upshot of this criticism is both to show the inadequacy of the classical foundationalist's criteria of proper basicality and to claim that there are no good reasons to suppose the proposition "God exists" cannot itself be accepted as properly basic. In fact, Plantinga informs us that the proper basicality of belief in God has been the long-standing practice of Reformed thinkers. But the strategy of Reformed thought invites the obvious question: If "God exists" is properly basic, what is to prevent someone from accepting any ludicrous belief as basic—that "the Great Pumpkin exists," for example? If, along with Plantinga and Reformed epistemologists, we affirm the acceptability of "God exists" as basic, then does anything go?

There are several points to notice in Plantinga's response to what he calls "the Great Pumpkin Objection." The first is that the critic tacitly supposes that in order to identify a proposition as basic one must have in hand a functioning criterion of proper basicality. But Plantinga, like Chisholm, denies this, pursuing instead the option of "particularism" rather than "methodism."[7] Stated simply, the particularist holds that one develops a criterion, say for proper basicality, by comparing it to examples one already considers properly basic. The criteria are subsequent to our already having gathered paradigmatic examples of properly basic beliefs. One then tests the adequacy of the criteria by reference to those examples. Why, then, says Plantinga, cannot our criteria be developed so as to include the proposition "God exists?"

More importantly, one should notice that although "God exists" is basic, (it does not rest on other beliefs adduced as evidence for it), it is not "groundless." For any basic belief $q, \ldots q_n$ there is a corresponding set of circumstances that spontaneously and non-inferentially gives rise to my belief and justifies me in my taking it as basic.

---

[7] See Roderick Chisholm's "The Problem of the Criterion," in *The Foundations of Knowing* (Minneapolis: University of Minnesota Press, 1982).

An example will help. Consider the belief, "I see a cat on the mat." Typically I do not hold such a belief on the basis of other beliefs; it is basic for me. But this belief is not groundless—it corresponds to an appropriate set of circumstances, namely, the experiences consisting of my being appeared to in an appropriate way; in this case "catly" and "matly." I shall let Plantinga speak for himself here:

> My being appeared to in this characteristic way (together with other circumstances) is what confers on me the right to hold the belief in question; this is what justifies me in accepting it. We could say, if we wish, that this experience is what justified me in holding it; this is the ground of my justification, and, by extension, the ground of the belief itself.[8]

How then does our awareness of the grounds of a belief help us to separate proper from improper basic beliefs? Well, in this way: properly basic beliefs are those which arise out of appropriate corresponding circumstances. Improperly basic beliefs lack the appropriate grounding experiences. So, to take the belief in the Great Pumpkin, we see that there is obviously no corresponding experience or state of affairs which serves as its grounds.

But what are the corresponding experiences which serve as the grounds of my belief that God exists? They are not, says Plantinga, the sublime experiences of the mystics: they are more commonplace experiences which include "feeling the presence of God," or "feeling as though God were speaking to one," or "being overcome with guilt and feeling as though God disapproved of my actions." These experiences would in turn give rise, respectively, to the following beliefs: God is near me; God is speaking to me; God disapproves of my actions. So, properly speaking, it is not "God exists" which is properly basic, but the aforementioned sort of beliefs, each of which entail that "God exists."

Plantinga's account for demarcating proper and improper basic beliefs raises several difficulties. One problem with Plantinga's account is that the precise relationship between the grounds for our belief and the belief itself is not adequately specified. We are told that upon experiencing something such as

---

[8]Plantinga, "Reason and Belief," p. 79.

(1) seeming to see a tree,

the corresponding belief

(2) "I see a tree"

arises immediately, spontaneously, and non-inferentially. Here the connection between ground and belief seems straightforward; but is it?

Consider a more complex sort of experience:

(3) seeming to see a man beating his wife.

Now can we specify in advance which corresponding belief should arise from such grounds?

(4) "I see a man beating his wife."

(5) "It is wrong to beat one's spouse."

(6) "I had better intervene in this marital squabble to protect the woman's rights"

Suppose I claimed (4), (5), and (6) are all basic for me, and furthermore I single out as their grounds one and the same state of affairs—that specified by (3). Is there anything wrong in so doing? Have I failed to exhibit the right connection between my grounds and beliefs? But what is this connection?

The case of religious beliefs proves equally complex. Consider the following experience an ordinary religious believer might have:

(7) feeling awe and majesty upon beholding God's creation.

Now precisely what basic belief is (7) the grounds for?

(8) "God is smart."

(9) "God is powerful."

(10) "God likes mountains."

Indeed, it seems hard to establish just what basic beliefs are supposed to arise out of what grounds. What remains mysterious about Plantinga's account is the input-output relation. In the presence of circumstance X, what belief should arise? Or is it possible that numerous beliefs can arise from one and the same experiential ground?

Let us focus on the following condition laid down by Plantinga. "In condition C, S is justified in taking P as basic." He does tell us that C will vary with P. So, to take a perceptual case, if I see a rose-colored wall before me, C will include my being appeared to in an appropriate way. But if I know I am wearing rose-colored glasses or am color-blind, I will not be justified in taking P as basic. This makes perfectly good sense. But in many perceptual cases, even those in which we are mistaken, we are not aware of any intervening condition that would cause us to question our right to take the corresponding belief in question as basic.

Consider the following situation: S stares into a crowd and seems to see a woman wearing jungle fatigues, sequined high-heels, and sporting waist-length pink hair. He immediately forms the corresponding belief:

(11) "I see a punk rocker."

However, an aerial photograph of the crowd taken at the precise moment of S's perceptual experience fails to reveal any person fitting this description. At the moment S is appeared to in the manner characteristic of the punk rocker, he immediately takes it as basic that he indeed sees a punker; and, we might add, justifiably so. But the *prima facie* justification that attaches to S's belief is defeated upon learning that his perception was not reliable. We are inclined to say that S was justified in taking (11) as basic until the moment he discovers his mistake. Perhaps it is situations like these which cause Plantinga to state:

So being appropriately appeared to, in the perceptual case, is not sufficient for justification; some further condition—a condition hard to state in detail—is clearly necessary.[9]

The condition which is so vexing to describe is one which specifies under what conditions a person S is justified in forming a basic belief upon having undergone a certain experience. It is a condition which monitors the input-output relation and specifies when that relation is sound. Without specifying what this condition is, it is hard to see how the following situation can be avoided:

A superstitious pumpkin farmer is out hoeing a patch of pumpkins at twilight. Suddenly he is overcome with a sense of the *mysterium tremendum* and promptly takes the following belief as basic:

(12) "There is a Great Pumpkin."

Or, more disconcertingly, a Jew witnessing the atrocities of a Nazi concentration camp immediately, spontaneously, and non-inferentially finds himself believing:

(13) "It is false that the God of Abraham, Isaac, and Jacob exists."

Despite the rarity of beliefs like (12) and (13), it is difficult to say just why they are not properly basic, given the corresponding circumstances experienced by the farmer and the Jew. It goes without saying that the imprecise character of religious experience exacerbates the problem. Or consider another case: two individuals undergo seemingly identical experiences; standing shoulder to shoulder both stare into a glorious star-filled sky. But in person A this experience immediately prompts the basic belief that God exists, while person B forms only the belief that he sees stars. Whose response, A or B's, is the correct one? Or are they both correct? Is either A or B deficient in some way?

In defense of Plantinga we can bring the old philosophical adage, "all perception is theory-laden." Perhaps the explanation behind two people's experiencing the same

---

[9]Ibid., p. 80.

circumstances yet forming different beliefs in response to them is that each possesses different background information that is crucial to the belief formation process. We should not think that a belief's basicality is impugned because of the interpretive role played in its formation. All it means to say that a belief is basic is that it is not logically dependent on any other belief for support. It is our experience *together* with our contextual beliefs that operate in the grounding process and justify the basic belief.

The relationship between grounds and belief can be further clarified by Plantinga's discussion of belief-dispositions. It seems that all human beings have dispositions, or natural tendencies, to believe certain things in the appropriate circumstances. Following Calvin, Plantinga believes that these dispositions are implanted in us by our Creator and include an innate tendency to believe that God exists. This disposition is universally present in mankind and is activated by the evidence of divine craftsmanship in nature. The spontaneous act of belief which is triggered in us by creation has been partly dulled by sin and is not so strong that we are unable to suppress it.

We must be careful to distinguish between belief dispositions and what are called alternatively by Reid "first principles," "the original principles of nature," "the principles of common sense," or just plain "common sense." Belief dispositions are the psychological mechanisms which are part of our God-given natural endowment whose output are the first principles of common sense. The technical workings of these belief dispositions are left unexplained by Reid.

> . . . all we can affirm certainly is, that nature hath established a constant conjunction between them and the things called their effects; and hath given to mankind a disposition to observe these connections, to confide in their continuance, and to make use of them for the improvement of our knowledge, and increase of our power.[10]

The input-output relation is mysterious even to Reid. I mention the difficulties surrounding the input-output relationship to underscore a problem that will be more acute as we consider the claim that doctrinal beliefs can be basic.

---

[10]Thomas Reid, *Inquiry and Essays*, ed. Beanblossom and Lehrer (Indianapolis: Hackett Publishing Co., 1983), chap. 5, sec. 3.

To summarize, given the bankruptcy of the classical foundationalist's criteria of proper basicality, we have explored an alternative way to determine which among our beliefs are truly basic, to wit, Plantinga's suggestion that corresponding to every properly basic belief are experiential grounds. Now we are in a position to ask what effect, if any, the appeal to basic beliefs has for doctrinal beliefs. Are they properly basic? Is it possible that someone could rightly take the proposition "God is triune" as basic? What possible sorts of experiential grounds could prompt or undergird such a belief?

REFORMED EPISTEMOLOGY AND DOCTRINAL BELIEFS

Reformed thinkers have taken not only belief in God as basic, but doctrinal beliefs as well. In fact, many Reformed thinkers have thought it appropriate to take Scripture in its entirety as basic. In so doing, the philosophers and theologians in question are saying neither that the truths of Scripture are self-evident nor without grounds. These basic beliefs are not arbitrarily adopted nor accepted on a merely provisional basis so that their formal relations can be drawn out. The beliefs which function basically for the Reformers arise out of experiential contexts. This theme pervades the writings of Reformed thinkers. To quote the Dutch theologian Bavinck:

> Scripture does not reason in the abstract. It does not make God the conclusion of a syllogism, leaving it to us whether we think the argument holds or not. But it speaks with authority. Both theologically and religiously, it proceeds from God as the starting point.[11]

Every academic discipline or science is grounded upon absolute presuppositions or axioms for which no proofs are offered. Theology is no different in this regard, and Reformed thinkers urge that we accept the Christian Scriptures as just such a starting point. In this vein Abraham Kuyper, a distinguished Dutch theologian and statesman,

---

[11]Herman Bavinck, *The Doctrine of God*, trans. William Hendricksen (Grand Rapids, MI: Wm. B. Eerdmans Publishing Co., 1951), pp. 78-79.

speaks of sacred Scripture as the *"principium theologiae."*[12] He who would learn of the central revelation by God's Spirit must seek it in Scripture. It is clear from Kuyper's writings that sacred Scripture is the supreme *principium* or set of basic beliefs next to which all others can only be viewed as auxiliaries. This is not to say that Scripture speaks to the special concerns of, say, the scientist by giving him actual scientific or experimental principles by which to act. But the content of Scripture does range over every human endeavor, and, so far as it addresses the ultimate ends for which mankind is destined, its influence must be supreme for any area of inquiry.

Plantinga informs us that the Reformers took God's existence as basic and were disdainful of any attempts to base such knowledge on the efforts of natural theology. But to what source, then, did the Reformers turn to acquire true knowledge of God? The answer is the self-attesting witness of Scripture. Calvin speaks unambiguously about the primacy of Scripture:

> If true religion is to beam upon us, our principle must be, that it is necessary to begin with heavenly teaching, and that it is impossible for any man to obtain even the minutest portion of right and sound doctrine without being a disciple of Scripture. Hence the first step in true knowledge is taken when we reverently embrace the testimony which God has been pleased therefore to give of himself.[13]

The picture that emerges from Reformed thought is this: not only is belief in the *Christian* God (not minimal theism) properly basic, but Scripture, the only source of true knowledge of God, is also properly basic. Calvin's view seems to be limited to the claim that Scripture is the final authority in matters of faith and practice. Another Reformed thinker, Cornelius Van Til (whose views are considered extreme by some Reformed thinkers), extends the primacy of Scripture to *all* intellectual endeavors; it is the hub around which general knowledge on any subject must turn.

---

[12]See Abraham Kuyper's *Encyclopedia of Sacred Theology*, trans. J. Hendrik De Vries (New York: Chas. Scribner's Sons, 1898), especially chapter II.

[13]John Calvin, *Institutes of the Christian Religion*, trans. H. Beveridge (Grand Rapids, MI: Wm. B. Eerdmans Publishing Co., 1981), Bk. 1, chap. VI, sect. 2.

Now it is, of course, true that many of the sciences do not, like theology proper, concern themselves with the question of religion. Granting this, it remains a matter of great significance that ultimately all the facts of the universe are either what they are because of their relation to the system of truth set forth in Scripture or they are not. In every discussion about every fact, therefore, it is the two principles, that of the believer in Scripture and that of the non-Christian, that stand over against one another. Both principles are totalitarian. Both claim all the facts. It is in the light of this point that the relation of the Bible as the infallible Word of God to the "facts" of science and history must finally be understood.[14]

Is the acceptance of Scripture properly basic? At first blush we are inclined to agree with the Reformed thinkers. Plantinga claims in "Reason and Belief in God" that a 14 year-old theist who has grown up within a religious community probably does and is entitled to take his belief in God as basic. But if Plantinga's 14 year-old theist is intellectually guiltless for taking God's existence as basic in a community where everyone believes, one can hardly blame him for accepting the primacy of Scripture right along with it. From childhood he observes the privileged position Scripture occupies in the daily life of his community. He hears it quoted at the dinner table, preached from the pulpit, is given rewards for memorizing it, and is instructed to seek guidance there for every aspect of his life. These activities do not function as evidence for the truth of Scripture; they merely facilitate its acceptance as a final authority. Does the 14 year-old theist stand in violation of his "all-things-considered" intellectual duty?

If every basic belief is connected to a set of experiential circumstances which serve as its grounds, then what sorts of experiential grounds prompt our doctrinal beliefs? One obvious candidate suggests itself: the miraculous. Surely our witnessing the altars of Baal being burned up by Elijah's God or beholding the resurrected body of Christ would spontaneously and non-inferentially produce belief in Yahweh as the true God and Jesus as the Messiah respectively. Witnesses of such phenomena do not *reason* from their occurrence to the beliefs to which they give rise. Rather they accept the corresponding beliefs immediately.

---

[14]Cornelius Van Til, *A Christian Theory of Knowledge* (Philadelphia: The Presbyterian and Reformed Publishing Co., 1975), p. 37.

But is the appeal to miracles simply a repetition of the evidentialist's tactic? Not necessarily. One way to view the relationship between a miracle and the propositional content of special revelation is in a strictly evidential manner. The signs and wonders move the intellect to assent insofar as they testify to feats capable of being accomplished only by God. But as the apologetics of the seventeenth and eighteenth centuries show, miracles at best provide only probabilistic support for the truth of revelation, for there is no strictly logical connection between them. It is at least possible, though improbable, that a person or power not representing God be capable of such deeds.

But firmer assent is possible if these signs are viewed not purely for the intrinsic evidential value they possess but as "natural signs," experiential data which immediately and spontaneously produce belief. The connection between sign and belief is like the activation of a belief disposition spoken of by Reid.

The degree of certainty attaching to a belief which is the result of a natural sign is not the same as the apodictic certainty of the syllogism. It would be a mistake to view the relationship between the miracle at Cana or the healing of the blind man and the truth of Jesus's teachings as a strictly evidential or logical one. No doubt it can be viewed this way; to do so is consonant with the apologetic concerns of thinkers like Locke, Paley, or Swinburne. Their task is to argue for the speculative credibility of the Christian faith based on miracles. Perhaps for some people the evidential approach is a necessary pre-condition for activating the disposition to believe on the basis of natural signs.

Let us assume that miracles can indeed function as natural signs; how does this advance the prospects of doctrinal beliefs being well grounded and properly basic? Unfortunately, the answer must be "very little." No doubt for any Christian having witnessed the miraculous first-hand, we can grant the justifiability of accepting as basic the teachings of the prophet who performs the miracle. It seems wholly appropriate for the revived Lazarus to accept Christ's teachings as basic. But most believers are not so blessed. They are neither the beneficiaries of nor witnesses to the miraculous. It seems, then, as in the evidentialist's case, that the road to justified doctrinal beliefs cannot be traveled by ordinary believers.

But perhaps this conclusion is premature.

Among the belief dispositions cited by Reid and discussed by Wolterstorff is the "credulity disposition."[15] In effect, we are automatically disposed to accept the testimony of others as true. This is a vital disposition for the developing child. But with age we encounter deception and false testimony and become discriminating as to whether this disposition will work its full effect on us. But the important point to notice is that beliefs which arise from this disposition and which we have no reason to doubt are thereby *prima facie* justified. If a mother tells her child that her missing toy can be found in the next room and the child has no reason to distrust her mother, then she naturally and automatically forms the corresponding belief—and justifiably so. Now suppose someone I have every reason to trust tells me that he has been the recipient of God's miraculous intervention and has been personal witness to such events. Unless I had reason for doubting his words, I would naturally take it as true that the events had occurred as described.[16] Such has been the situation of Christian believers from the Apostolic era. So St. John wrote:

> We are writing to you about something which has always existed yet which we ourselves actually saw and heard: something which we had opportunity to observe closely and even to hold in our hands, and yet, as we know now, was something of the very Word of Life Himself! For it was Life which appeared before us: we saw it, we are eye-witnesses of it, and are now writing to you about it.[17]

The suggestion before us is this: since personal acquaintance with the miraculous is unavailable to the average believer, its usefulness as a ground for the acceptance of Scripture is thereby limited. However, it may be sufficient that we are *told* about such

---

[15]See Wolterstorff's "Thomas Reid on Rationality," in *Rationality in the Calvinian Tradition*, ed. Hart, Van Derhoeven, and Wolterstorff (Lanham, MD: University Press of America, 1983).

[16]Phil Quinn has argued recently that no sophisticated adult in today's society can take such beliefs as basic in the face of so many potential defeaters we have good reasons for thinking are true. See "In Search for the Foundations of Theism," *Faith and Philosophy* 2 (1985). A response from Plantinga can be found in *Faith and Philosophy* 3 (1986):298-313.

[17]I John 1:1-2. Phillips translation.

states of affairs. Of course, there are differences between the two grounds, both in their degree of vivacity and in the extent to which they give rise to belief. Obviously, if I am a personal eye-witness to a miraculous event, the degree to which I am impelled to accept the corresponding beliefs is stronger than if such events were made known to me only through testimony. Similarly, the *prima facie* justification attaching to such beliefs is less easily overridden in the eye-witness account, there being less chance of my being mistaken or deceived about such things.

Perhaps, then, the evidentialist appeal to miracles is entirely unnecessary—to be *prima facie* justified in one's belief, say, in the Trinity, all that is needed is that I am told it is true and that I believe what I am told. Perhaps as children we are simply told that God is triune, and this is sufficient to justify the belief. Then, upon reaching a state of maturity in age and belief, we can look back upon a life lived in accordance with such doctrines and appeal to a kind of retrospective justification if necessary.[18] We might add that the fact that I see no reason to give up the belief is itself grounds for the belief.

Unfortunately, this suggestion raises severe difficulties. It is certainly true that the credulity-disposition contributes significantly to our stockpile of beliefs. I grant, moreover, that testimony is usually sufficient to justify much of what we believe. But it is unlikely that testimony can bear the load Wolterstorff requires of it. For surely I cannot accept a belief as basic on the testimony of others if I cannot understand what is being proposed for acceptance. If I am told that "Pink sleep strolls merrily upstream" it would not be permissible to take this proposition as a basic belief no matter how

---

[18]The idea behind retrospective justification is this: As Christians, we believe certain things about God's nature and intentions for us. We thereby anticipate that God will manifest Himself in our experience in certain ways. And when our expectations are realized, we view this as a kind of confirmation of our beliefs. For example, the believer holds that by living his life in accordance with certain beliefs, he can expect his character to be transformed in certain ways. When his expectations are realized, he has greater reason for thinking that the beliefs which informed his expectations are true. For an excellent and detailed defense of this manner of confirming the Christian's faith see William Alston's "Christian Experience and Christian Belief," in *Faith and Rationality*.

reliable I thought the source. If a mother tells a child, "God is triune," we have a similar situation. It is unlikely that what the child has accepted as basic is the belief in the Trinity. Probably what is accepted by the child is the belief, "My mother's words express some truth," or "Whatever my mother told me must be true." The content of the statement, "God is triune" is not what is accepted as basic, since to the small child it makes no more sense than the nonsense statement above.[19]

It would appear, then, that a necessary condition of our accepting as basic some proposition received from testimony is that we understand what is said. We should be minimally aware of its conditions of assertability and truth. No doubt understanding in this sense is a matter of degree. But it is doubtful that the doctrines of the faith could be basic under this restriction. It might therefore be lamented that more believers are not the recipients of direct rather than indirect contact with the divine.

But maybe this assessment is hasty. A major theme in the Reformed tradition is that the man in the pew is, indeed, directly acquainted with God. Reformed thinkers teach that all believers are recipients of a more generic religious experience; an experience, moreover, which vouchsafes the truth of Scripture. Against those who think the inspired status of Scripture rests on our first having acquired sufficient evidence, Calvin writes:

> But I answer that the testimony of the Spirit is superior to reason. For as God alone can properly bear witness to his own words, so these words will not obtain full credit in the hearts of men, until they are sealed by the inward testimony of the Spirit.[20]

And Kuyper tells us how the testimony of the Holy Spirit directly assures us of the divine quality of Scripture, a testimony that goes "directly from the Holy Spirit, as author of the Scripture, to our personal ego."[21] By this act of enlightenment, Kuyper tells us, the Holy Spirit illumines the mind, bringing to consciousness a clear belief in

---

[19]In saying this I am not denying the fittingness of Augustine's "I believe in order to understand." The understanding of which Augustine speaks is not the same as the minimal awareness of a proposition's intelligibility, but rather a profound recognition bordering on self-evidence.

[20]Calvin, *Institutes*, p. 72.

[21]Kuyper, *Encyclopedia of Sacred Theology*, p. 557. See also chapter 1, sections 5 and 6 of the *Westminster Confession*.

both the inspired and divine nature of Scripture. To this we might add the experiences of people like Karl Barth, who speak of being called or hearing the voice of God when reading the Bible.

Here at last may be the sort of grounds which automatically give rise to a corresponding belief in the truths attested to in Scripture. By the experience of the Holy Spirit's "bearing witness with our spirit" (Rom. 8:16) we spontaneously and immediately assent to portions of Scripture as the Word of God. So, in actuality, it is not a specific doctrine to which the testimony of the Holy Spirit gives rise. It is rather the wholesale acceptance of certain passages of Scripture as coming from God. So from our acceptance of the Scriptures, we proceed, through theological deliberation, to derive specific doctrinal beliefs. So then, we have the Reformer's affirmative answer to the question of whether or not our acceptance of the Scriptures is properly basic: yes, insofar as they arise or are activated by the Spirit's work within us, an experience presumably accessible to all believers.

An important qualification is in order. Though the Reformers claim that their acceptance of the Scriptures is basic, this does not imply that the content of every proposition of Scripture is perspicuous. It does not preclude their admitting to the need for a hermeneutic. My taking the Scriptures as basic does not imply that I understand or accept at face value every proposition in the Bible, though it would seem some understanding of its content is necessary. It could still be admitted that a proper understanding of Scripture's content hinges on meticulous study and reflection.

Again it would be a mistake to construe the activity of the Spirit as providing new or "private evidence" for the truths of Scripture. Neither does the Spirit necessarily bring us into a better awareness of already existing evidence. Both construals would reduce to a position very much like the evidentialist's. For if the Spirit provides us with new evidence, there would seem to be no reason why this could not be made known to others—say, non-believers. The correct interpretation of the inward prompting must be viewed as God's deliberately activating a belief disposition to accept His word as true. Of course, this is a disposition which the Reformers say has suffered from the debilitating effects of sin and must, therefore, be directly activated by God.

ASSESSMENT OF THE REFORMED TRADITION

But now it seems that we have come full circle (and a large circle it is!). We began with the suggestion that Christians can legitimately take their doctrinal beliefs as basic. This prompted us to ask what experiences might serve as the grounds for these beliefs. The answer given was that we may rightfully take as basic that the Scriptures (from which our doctrines are derived) are the revelation of God when we experience the interior illumination of the Spirit. But is not the belief that we are being illumined by the Spirit as problematic as the belief for which it serves as grounds? Even if we grant that we have a belief disposition to accept the content of Scripture as basic when this disposition is activated by the Holy Spirit, the justification it confers is, at best, only weakly *prima facie*. Just as we can be deceived by yielding to the credulity-disposition, so, too, we have good reason to ask if the illumining activity of the Spirit is real, or simply the result of indigestion or enthusiasm. Must the Christian be able to show that the illumination is genuine? And what sorts of indications might he give that it is? Would this not once again involve us in the difficulties that embroiled the evidentialist approach to justifying doctrinal beliefs? Or maybe the belief that we are being illumined by the Holy Spirit is itself basic. Then what are the grounds out of which this belief arises?

In defense of the Reformed position it can be pointed out that one does not have to *know* he is justified in order to *be* justified, just as knowledge does not depend on "knowing that one knows." But does it follow from this that any feeling we call the interior illumination of the Spirit is authentic? Surely some conditions must be satisfied. Minimally, the grounds which undergird S's belief that he is illumined must not be believed by S to be delusory or in some way defective. If S has good reason to think that his belief that he is illumined is the product of wish-fulfillment, then it cannot rightfully serve as the grounds for anything.[22] Secondly, while it would be excessive

---

[22]This condition is admittedly weak. Given that some people are prone to deceive themselves about religious matters, the mere fact that a person does not believe that his illumination is the product of wish-fulfillment is not a very strong guarantee that it is genuine. His belief may be unjustified because he is the victim of a long history of self-deception and is now unable to discriminate between authentic experiences and those produced by wish-fulfillment. We would still want to say that such a person is guilty of intellectual wrongdoing.

to demand that one prove in some absolute sense that the illumination is genuine, it nevertheless must be the case that my *experience* of the illumination is genuine. That is, I must myself be convinced that the experience has not been conjured up or is not the product of self-deception. Precisely what criteria are necessary for us to personally vouchsafe our experience is difficult to state.

Thomas Reid, from whom the Reformed epistemologists seem to draw much inspiration, is no ally of the suggestion before us, namely, that we have a belief-disposition to embrace the totality of Scripture as divine upon experiencing the illumination of the Spirit. If all it takes to justify a belief is to call it the product of a belief-producing mechanism, then we will open the floodgates and trivialize the very notion of a justified belief. Are there no constraints on what sorts of beliefs may be properly called the products of innate belief-dispositions?

One way to tell whether we have the innate psychological faculty in question is to see whether or not there is a corresponding first principle to which it can be linked. Reid provides several criteria for the proper identification of first principles:[23]

1. Self-evidence—Reid sometimes means by this immediately accepted upon being understood, and other times, immediately accepted upon having an experience of a certain sort (*EIP* I, 2; II, 20).

2. Irresistibility— those who deny them are considered mad (*EIP* I, 2; II, 20).

3. Universal Agreement—a consensus among the learned and unlearned (*EIP* I, 2).

4. Determined by our nature—genuine belief-producing mechanisms are constitutive of our nature and their output accepted in a pre-philosophical manner (*EIP* II, 20).

---

[23]This list can be found in Thomas Reid's *Essays On the Intellectual Powers of Man in Thomas Reid's Inquiry and Essays,* ed. Ronald Beanblossem and Keith Lehrer (Indianapolis: Hackett Publishing Co., 1983). An excellent discussion of Reid's first principles can be found in William Alston's "Thomas Reid on Epistemic Principles" *History of Philosophy Quarterly* 2 (1985).

As momentary reflection on these criteria will show, not only is the acceptance of Scripture as divine not a first principle, but neither is the minimal belief that God exists! Though Reid thought God's existence provable from first principles, it is not itself among the first principles. It is clear that Reid's criteria would rule out the suggestion before us.

Perhaps it will be retorted that those of the Reformed view enjoy the merit of knowing when to part company with Reid. The reason God's existence and the divinity of His Word are not irresistible, universally accepted, and so forth, is that humans have been blinded by sin. They have deliberately squelched the natural operation of their God-given noetic equipment.

This sort of a response is frustrating for several reasons. First, it is epistemologically sectarian; it has no purchase on those who do not already accept it. Secondly, it appears epistemologically circular. The belief that sin has caused us to distort our natural intellectual endowment is a part of the very revelation whose epistemic status is at issue! That we are so blinded is a piece of information that cannot be had without relying on the very Scripture whose status as revelation is under question![24]

While it must be admitted that the Reformed response is dialectically deficient, that is, unsuitable for the purposes of argumentation, it is difficult to see that it fails to secure personal justification. Thus, I am led to the conclusion that the Reformed believer can be minimally justified in his doctrinal beliefs. But while the Reformed view may be adequate to secure personal justification, it seems unsuited for apologetical tasks.

Justification construed as involving positive epistemic status, unlike the weaker notion of permissive justification, is more closely allied with concerns of truth. While the strategy of the Reformed epistemologist may secure personal entitlement, it seems less plausible to grant that it also confers a stronger type of justification—one that is necessary, perhaps, for knowledge. To the accusation, "You are committing intellectual sin," the Reformed epistemologist has a ready response. To the question, "How do you know that what you believe is true?" the Reformed strategy seems of little help.

It also comes to mind to ask whether the advances of the Reformed view profit the individual believer. A major problem with the evidentialist is that the amount and kind of evidence needed to justify doctrinal belief surpasses the grasp of the ordinary

---

[24]Plantinga seems to be aware that such a response will not be polemically useful. See "Reason and Belief In God," p. 77.

believer. The advantage of the Reformed view is that it presumably places justification within reach of the ordinary "man in the pew." Or does it? Is the ordinary Calvinist equipped to respond to objections that his belief in God is not properly basic? Is the *prima facie* warrant for the belief in God removed upon one's finding out that many other Christians take neither their belief that God exists nor their doctrinal beliefs as basic? Does a religiously pluralistic society such as ours provide sufficiently unfavorable or defeating conditions for our taking doctrinal beliefs as basic?

Again, the believer does not have to show that he is justified to be justified. The average Reformed believer can be justified in taking his belief in God as basic though he has never self-consciously framed this concept. But we are considering the case of the astute Calvinist who is not only aware of the manner in which his faith is held, but finds himself unable to respond to criticism that he ought not hold it in that way. Is the Calvinist now thrust into the position of having to rebut objections to belief in order to be justified?

I think it is too stringent to demand that the average Calvinist, when faced with an apparently defeating argument, find positive reasons to rebut the premises of his opponents' arguments. It is sufficient for him to show that for *him* the potential defeater has no force. Buoyed by the fact that highly trained Reformed philosophers have considered the objections in question and not found them undermining, the ordinary believer is given reason to think his opponents' arguments are unsound. In a way, it can be said that the unsophisticated believer obtains his justification vicariously, deriving benefit from the fact that the champions of his faith have considered the very objections he faces and remained unscathed.

My criticisms notwithstanding, I am inclined to think that the views of the Reformed thinkers, rather than these of the evidentialists, show greater promise for providing the minimal justification the ordinary believer seeks. But if the believer seeks justification of a stronger sort and aspires to feats greater than negative apologetics, then it would seem that some concessions will have to be made to the strategies of the evidentialist.

Apologetics In A New Key:
Relieving Protestant Anxieties
Over Natural Theology

C. Stephen Evans

St. Olaf College

Many Protestants, especially those in the Reformed and Lutheran traditions, have historically been cool or hostile to natural theology and often to the whole enterprise of evidentialist apologetics. By "natural theology" I have in mind the enterprise of attempting to prove or show the reasonableness of belief in God apart from acceptance of any religious authority, and by "evidentialist apologetics" I mean the larger enterprise of attempting to show the reasonableness of Christian faith, of which natural theology might naturally be seen as a significant component. Roughly, the natural theologian attempts to demonstrate the reasonableness of belief in God; the evidentialist apologist then goes on to attempt to show it is reasonable to believe that God has revealed Himself in the ways Christians believe, pre-eminently in Jesus Christ. To simplify my discussion I shall focus on natural theology, but I believe that many of the points made are relevant to the more general project.

In this essay I shall try to lay out some of the reasons Protestants have been suspicious of natural theology. I shall try to show that none of the reasons warrants rejecting natural theology in particular or evidentialist apologetics in general. However, some of the objections to the project do require us to carefully limit and qualify the enterprise. Thinking through the objections gives us a better understanding of the strengths and the limitations of rational arguments for faith.

Just why have so many Protestants been suspicious of natural theology? I believe that the most important reasons fall into five types. I shall briefly list the types and then respond in detail to the arguments individually.

OBJECTIONS TO NATURAL THEOLOGY

1. **The "noetic effects of sin" argument.** The fall has so harmed our natural faculties, including reason, as to make it impossible to gain any natural knowledge of God.

2. **The "reason as presumption" argument.** Trying to gain a natural knowledge of God fosters a sinful autonomy on the part of human beings.

3. **The "superfluity" argument.** Special revelation provides a quicker and surer way to the knowledge of God.

4. **The "god of the philosophers" argument.** Natural theology leads to an abstract, philosophical God who is remote from genuine religious concerns.

5. **The "arguments aren't very good" argument.** Arguments for God's existence are lousy; using such arguments fosters unbelief by making belief in God appear shaky.

RESPONSES TO OBJECTIONS

1. Let us first consider the "noetic effects of sin" argument. The objection assumes that natural theology rests on the dubious claim that the fall corrupted only part of the human personality, say, the will and emotions, leaving reason basically intact. If it were true that natural theology rested on such an assumption, I would be the first to throw it out, since it seems to me that we have massive empirical evidence that the way people reason is affected by their sinful attitudes and desires. However, I do not think that natural theology requires any such assumption.

Suppose that we assume that the Calvinist doctrine of total depravity is correct. Even on this assumption, it does not follow that natural theology is impossible. Total depravity has never been taken to mean that human beings are as bad as they could be in every respect. Rather, it means that human sinfulness extends to the totality of the human personality; no particular area is exempt from the damaging effects of sin.

Obviously, what follows from this is not that human reason can never gain any knowledge of anything, or that all human reasoning is worthless. It follows only that much human reasoning is likely to be defective. This implies that natural theology may be difficult. Both the ones attempting to do the natural theology and the ones who are supposed to be convinced may be harmed or blinded by their sinfulness. But surely this does not mean that natural theology is impossible, any more than sinfulness implies that nothing valuable and useful can be accomplished by the human will. This implies that natural theologians should be modest and open to criticism; it means that their efforts are not guaranteed success. It does not mean that their efforts are guaranteed to be failures.

2. The "reason as presumption" argument sees natural theology not so much blocked from success by sin, but rather as itself an expression of sin. This critic, rightly understanding sin as prideful presumption, a rebellious attempt on the part of human beings to declare their independence from God, interprets natural theology as part of the problem rather than part of the solution.

After all, thinks the critic, does not natural theology involve an assumption that unaided human reason can discover ultimate truth on its own? And does not the natural theologian exhibit a disdain for the humble acceptance of divine authority when he attempts to make discoveries about God on the basis of his reason, rather than divine revelation? And does not the whole enterprise suggest that reason itself has been placed in the position of receiving our ultimate allegiance, since the natural theologian seems to suggest that God is to be recognized and worshiped only if He measures up to our rational tests?

Actually, the critic makes several assumptions of his own here, which are dubious on a closer look. First, let us look at the charge that natural theology is prideful because it relies on unaided human reason rather than revelation. Why assume that human reason in attempting to gain knowledge about God is always unaided? Reason is itself a gift of God, and there is no reason God could not assist the reasoner in trying to come to some knowledge about God. In fact, it is perfectly consistent for the natural theologian to approach his project with prayer for such divine assistance, both for himself and for those he hopes to persuade.

The assumption that natural theology is inherently prideful looks dubious also, if natural theology can be done in a spirit of prayer. The claim that natural theology is an expression of human autonomy and rebelliousness seems false if what the natural theologian is attempting to show is that human beings are essentially dependent on God.

The claim that the natural theologian is placing human reason above God as an idol also seems false, if it is claimed that this is necessary for natural theology. It must be granted that human beings are quite capable of idolatry and, therefore, quite capable of making an idol of human reason. Perhaps this is a constant temptation. But it does not seem right to me that one is automatically doing this by seeking to find truth about God through rational means.

Consider an analogous argument that a critic might give to the effect that Christians who accept the Bible as their final authority for the knowledge of God thereby place the Bible above God. Such an argument seems to me to rest on a confusion. The Bible may be the highest means I have for coming to know God, but it does not follow from this that the Bible has become for me a rival which has edged out God for my devotion. Rather the Bible is a means to finding out about God, who remains my supreme Lord.

In an analogous way, reason may be a means for finding out about God without this implying it has become an idol. The natural theologian does not have to hold that natural theology is the only way to find out about God or even that it is the best way. So it is not true that the natural theologian must view worship of God as conditioned by reason. I know of no reason to think that the rational powers God has given to human beings could not be a means God uses to enable us to come to know some things about Him.

3. The "natural theology is superfluous" argument maintains that natural theology is simply a waste of time. Nothing can be known in this way that cannot be known more surely from special revelation. Besides, the critic may say, it is God's grace that draws people to faith, not reason.

This last claim can be swiftly answered. It is certainly God's grace that draws people to faith, but who can maintain with certainty that God cannot use reason as one of the channels for His grace to draw people?

As for the claim that natural theology is superfluous if we have special revelation, there is a sense in which this may be conceded by the advocate of natural theology.

Thomas Aquinas, renowned as an advocate of natural theology, expressly maintained that special revelation which is received by faith does constitute a surer, more certain way of coming to know God, even in those cases in which the same truth can be known by reason.

I would go so far as to say that in an unfallen world, there would be no need for natural theology at all. This is somewhat surprising, since the critics of natural theology sometimes maintain that in an unfallen world natural theology would be acceptable. (See objection 1 above.) I do not mean by this merely what Alvin Plantinga and other advocates of "Reformed epistemology" have claimed, namely that in an unfallen world people would believe in God spontaneously and without the need for arguments, though this view may well be correct.

What I mean is rather that in a fallen world, unbelief may simply block a person from even considering the possibility of special revelation. If someone is absolutely convinced that God does not exist and that miracles are impossible, it is difficult to persuade him that he ought to believe in God because belief in God is taught in the Bible. Claiming that the Bible is the word of God and that it is attested by miracles is unlikely to have much impact either.

Of course, one may maintain that natural theology is unlikely to move such a person either, and that may be true in most cases. In principle, however, it would appear possible to engage this person by inquiring into the grounds of his certainty that God does not exist. If one could find premises which such a person accepts which make God's existence plausible, or at least not unreasonable, one might at least be able to shake up the skeptic's dogmatic confidence in atheism. If God's existence is at least plausible and if miracles are at least possible, then special revelation might get more of a real hearing.

4. The "god of the philosophers" argument maintains that natural theology does not lead to the God of Abraham, Isaac, and Jacob, but to a philosophical abstraction, an unmoved mover or necessary being who is divorced from the concerns of genuine human beings.

This objection has two forms. One might argue that the god of natural theology is actually inconsistent with the biblical picture of God. Alternatively, one might argue that the god of natural theology is simply incomplete, too thin and ghostly to do much religious work.

The first charge is more serious than the second. There is evidence, I think, that philosophical theology has sometimes sold out the biblical concept of God by reinterpreting biblical teachings in accord with philosophical demands. Some argue, for example, that such claims as that God is utterly outside time, that He is absolutely immutable, and that He is completely "impassible" (unable to be affected by anything outside Himself) are incompatible with the biblical data. However, all these charges are hotly disputed, and the proponents of these views of God defend them on both biblical and philosophical grounds. The truth is that the biblical picture of God is complex, requiring judgments as to what is literal and what is symbolic and interpretations of difficult texts. It is inevitable, and proper, that extra-biblical beliefs, including philosophical convictions, will play a role in shaping these interpretations. My conclusion is that although there is a danger of natural theology's distorting our biblical picture of God, this is only a danger, not a certainty. The charge must be made out for particular aspects of God, and even there it may be difficult to be clear about the truth. Is it certain, for instance, whether the Bible teaches that God is eternal in the sense of being everlasting or eternal in the sense of being timeless? And one must also recognize that philosophical thinking may not always be a distorting factor in understanding the biblical teaching, but might in some cases provide the needed clues as to what is central and what is peripheral, what is literal and what is symbolic.

The other form of the "god of the philosophers" argument, that natural theology leads to a truncated view of God, seems to me to be correct, but this is not fatal to natural theology. Natural theology, conceived as part of an apologetic enterprise, does not need to lead to a complete view of God. It needs only to discomfit the atheist and agnostic, suggest the plausibility of thinking there is something transcendent of the natural order, something that has some of the characteristics of the Christian God. That task is one natural theology certainly tries to accomplish and, on the surface, does so. God is conceived as cause and sustainer of the universe, designer of the order we see around us, foundation of the moral law. While hardly a full picture of God, these characteristics do correspond to recognizable aspects of God as conceived by Christians.

In fact, a natural theologian might well reject the common picture of natural theology as an enterprise in which a conception of God is to be manufactured from scratch. Instead, he might take the full-blooded Christian conception of God as a "given" hypothesis. It is true that the whole of this conception cannot be defended by natural theology. But it is often true that a web of scientific theories cannot be tested at every point, but only at certain points. The natural theologian's arguments can be viewed as attempts to test the Christian conception at particular points where it makes contact with human experience. Of course, the whole conception cannot be shown conclusively to be true in this way, but one might argue that the whole conception is thereby made more plausible, if the Christian conception is interconnected in the appropriate way.

5. The last of the objections to natural theology I wish to consider is the simplest and perhaps the most plausible. This is the claim that the arguments simply are not very good. Putting forward weak arguments leaves the impression that faith in God rests on shaky foundations, so that the net result of natural theology is to weaken rather than strengthen faith.

In one sense the only adequate response to this objection is simply to *do* natural theology in detail and show that the arguments have worth and that objections can be met. Such a comprehensive project lies far outside the scope of this essay. However, I do think some things can be said about natural theology in general which help to meet this objection. If natural theology is to be judged a success, it is essential that it be judged by appropriate standards.

Let us assume, in the spirit of adventure and as an experiment, that God exists and that He does make Himself known by reason, perhaps as one way among others of allowing us to know some things about Him. How, in general, would we expect such knowledge to come about? How would a God who wished to make Himself known by reason do so?

Any answer we give will, of course, be speculative and uncertain, for we are not God. Nevertheless, two points seem highly plausible to me.

The first is that if God has provided rational evidence of His reality, that evidence would be widely available, not restricted to those with esoteric knowledge or understandable only to those with great philosophical erudition. This is plausible if we assume that God wants the knowledge of Him to be widespread, and that He has no great partiality to the learned, both of which assumptions seem consistent with the biblical picture of God.

The second characteristic I would expect to find in the evidence God has provided for Himself, if He has provided any, is that the evidence would be *resistable* or *discountable*. This characteristic might seem to contradict the first one of being widely available, but I do not think that it does. To say that the evidence is resistable is not to say that it is hard to find or takes great learning to recognize, but rather to say that it is the kind of evidence which can be dismissed or explained away if the person wants to do so.

Now why do I think God would give us such resistable evidence? I think it is obvious that if God has given us rational evidence, the evidence is in fact resistable. The proof of that is simply that so many people manage to resist it. But I think that we can see good reasons why God would want to make the evidence for His reality resistable.

If God is indeed all-powerful and all-knowing, and if He has a right to our obedience and worship and has commanded us to follow His will, it is easy to see that many people, whether they truly wished to serve God or not, would choose to serve Him, out of fear of punishment or desire for external rewards. I do not believe that this is the kind of service God wants from us. He wants us to serve Him freely out of love. If His presence were too obvious, even wicked people might well obey Him, for very bad reasons. If this is correct, then it makes sense to suppose that God might give us evidence which is plenty adequate for the person who is seeking God and willing to serve Him, but is discountable for the person who is not willing to believe. This view allows a meaningful role in the whole enterprise to faith, which in this context could be characterized as that willingness to believe in God and serve God which is the condition for rightly viewing the evidence. Faith in this case would not be blind; there is evidence to which faith can respond. But the evidence is ineffective for the individual who lacks the proper kind of "subjectivity."

If we ask what kind of evidence this could be, I think the general answer is that it will be evidence which requires interpretation. There are plenty of good examples of discountable or resistable evidence in other spheres of life. Arguments over historical causes or art criticism are often very strong and can be conclusive for those who possess the requisite personal qualifications for evaluating them. Arguments in a law court are in a similar position. Such arguments can be strong ones. But they can only be recognized to be strong by the person who is a good judge of such things, the individual who can interpret the evidence rightly. I should expect the evidence for God to be like this: evidence which can point the sincere seeker in the right direction securely, but also allows the one who is rebelling against God to convince himself that religion contains no truth.

NATURAL THEOLOGY IN A NEW KEY

If we apply these insights to natural theology, what is the result? I think one plausible answer to this question is to think of the evidence that God has provided for His reality as consisting of *natural signs*. A natural sign is a pointer or clue to God's reality. It is a phenomenon which naturally suggests, to the person who is willing to believe in God, that God is indeed real. But since a natural sign is a sign, an indicator, it does not lead to a coercive proof. Someone who is so inclined can find other ways of reading and interpreting the sign.

On this view the traditional philosophical arguments for God's existence can be seen as attempts to articulate these natural signs and formulate them as rigorous arguments. I see nothing wrong with the attempt to do this. But it is a mistake to regard them as *proofs*. And it is a mistake to think that they are without value if they fail as conclusive proofs. The natural signs which the arguments are attempting to articulate retain their value as God's calling cards, even if a particular attempt to articulate the sign fails, when judged by a certain standard of proof. (A standard which, by the way, hardly any interesting argument in philosophy measures up to anyway.) The arguments may fail as proofs in the sense that they fail to convince all sane, rational persons, because not all sane, rational persons may have the personal qualities which are necessary to recognize the evidence as good evidence.

What are these pointers, or clues, or calling cards? I have already hinted that they correspond quite closely to the traditional theistic arguments. I would divide them into two major categories: signs which are apparent in that part of nature which is outside of ourselves and signs which are evident in human nature. I have attempted to describe these natural signs in some detail in the first half of my book, *The Quest for Faith: Reason and Mystery as Pointers to God.*[1]

---

[1]C. Stephen Evans, *The Quest for Faith: Reason and Mystery as Pointers to God* (Downers Grove, IL: Inter-Varsity Press, 1986).

The signs in nature correspond to the cosmological and teleological arguments, respectively. The cosmological argument is an attempt to come to terms with the experience I call the experience of cosmic wonder. In this experience we are suddenly struck with how surprising it is that we exist, that the things we see around us exist, that anything at all exists. Though this is in one sense an easily discountable experience, it can plausibly be interpreted as an experience of the createdness of the natural order, a clue which God has planted in our experience which points back to Himself.

The design in nature is an even more powerful clue. Even critics of the teleological argument, such as Hume and Kant, have been forced to recognize how natural and reasonable it seems to view the natural order as the work of a purposive mind, when we contemplate the starry heavens or the incredible intricacy of biological systems. Scientific knowledge, when not permeated by the desire of the unbelieving heart to discount any faith in God, only deepens our appreciation of the wonderfulness of nature and the tendency to see nature as pointing beyond itself.

The clues within ourself lie in three major areas, I think. First, there is the experience of the moral "ought," a clue which C. S. Lewis articulated so clearly and so effectively in *Mere Christianity*.[2] Secondly, there are the traces of the image of God in human persons. If human beings were really made by God in His image, then we would expect humans to transcend nature in certain respects, even while remaining solidly creatures. I believe that in the human capacity for creative, free activity we see just the kind of partial transcendence we would expect to find.

Finally, a strong clue to God's reality can be seen in our own desires. There is really a God-shaped hole in the human personality. If God has made us to enjoy fellowship with Himself, then it is reasonable to think that He would have instilled a fundamental desire for Himself. In *The Quest for Faith* I argue that the human desires for eternal life, for eternal meaning, and to be eternally loved, are in reality a desire for God. Of course, since humans are sinners, they also have a desire not to know God, a desire to cover over and obscure their desire for God from themselves, and this is a desire which is amply illustrated in human life. But for the discerning interpreter, the natural sign is still there.

All of these clues are widely available, recognizable by the simple as well as the learned. Any or all of these clues may be discounted, easily so when taken individually,

---

[2]C.S. Lewis, *Mere Christianity* (New York: Macmillan, 1952).

less easily so when considered together. Taken collectively they provide a cumulative case for the reasonableness of believing in God which is powerful for him who has ears to hear and eyes to see. However, recognizing the important role faith plays in their reception should make us sensitive to the fact that apologetic strategy must always focus on the person, not merely the argument. It is just as important to help the person become the sort of person who can recognize the evidence as it is to provide the evidence. And that task is not one which can be carried out by argument alone.

Of course, ultimately it is God who makes it possible for the person to hear and see. Faith is His work, not our own. But it is part of God's graciousness and goodness that He sometimes works through us in bringing His chosen ones into His fold. He helps people gain a willingness to respond to Himself by showing them His love through our love. And He helps people gain a clearer perception of His reality by allowing us to point to the pointers He has provided.

None of this implies that natural theology is essential for faith, and it certainly does not imply that natural theology has much value by itself. But it does imply that in a secular culture such as our own, natural theology might sometimes play a useful if limited role by challenging the dogmatic assumption that we live in a closed universe and thereby opening people to the possibility of a God who might reveal Himself in more special, personal terms.

An Epistemological Argument For the Existence Of God

Robert Tad Lehe

North Central College

In *The Resurrection of Theism* and in his more recent work, *The Reconstruction of the Christian Revelation Claim*,[1] Stuart C. Hackett defends versions of the cosmological, teleological, and moral arguments, inferring God's existence from the actuality of the cosmos, the orderliness of the cosmos, and the existence of persons and the moral order. An interesting form of argument briefly developed in *Reconstruction* is what Hackett calls a conceptual argument from the possibility of the cosmos. An even briefer version of this kind of argument was presented in *Resurrection of Theism* as a "reconstruction" of the ontological argument. In these arguments Hackett maintains that the possibility of the existence of any cosmos at all which could be knowable to us requires the endowment of the mind with *a priori* categories and principles, the ultimate ground of which can only reside in a transcendent, absolute Mind. This argument, as Hackett presents it, is a metaphysical argument in that it infers the existence of God as a condition of the possibility of the existence of the cosmos.

---

[1] Stuart C. Hackett, *The Resurrection of Theism* (Chicago: Moody Press, 1957); *The Reconstruction of the Christian Revelation Claim* (Grand Rapids, MI: Baker Book House, 1984).

But the argument moves to its conclusion by way of a premise which is heavily charged with epistemological theory. Thus it suggests the possibility of a more directly epistemological argument for theism, which I shall attempt to develop in this paper. In short, I shall argue for God's existence from the possibility of knowledge. The argument will proceed within the context of epistemological views to which Hackett is, I think, congenial. I am indebted to him for the inspiration for the argument, although I may only hope, and not know, that he would endorse it.

In *The Resurrection of Theism,* Hackett defends the coherence theory of truth, according to which theory coherence is the ultimate criterion of truth. In this paper I shall discuss the coherence theory and explore its implications for a defense of theism. The first section of the paper will develop in broad outline a version of the coherence theory similar to that which Hackett defends. According to this theory, rational justification of propositions involves incorporating them into a coherent and comprehensive system. The justification of the system involves the evaluation of it in light of the ideal of perfect systematic coherence. In the second section of the paper I shall argue that coherence is the criterion of truth and defend the coherence theory against some of the principal objections to it. In the third section I shall consider one of the most difficult problems with the coherence theory, that of the impossibility of realizing the ideal of a perfectly coherent system. If this ideal cannot be attained, then it is difficult to see how our incomplete, limited systems can be evaluated in light of it or how such limited systems can be compared with a perfectly coherent system. It is this problem which suggests an argument for the existence of God. The hypothesis that an infinite Mind exists, possesses a perfectly coherent and comprehensive grasp of reality, and is the source of our own minds, suggests itself as a way of accounting for a relationship between our limited systems and the ideal of a perfectly coherent system. That the hypothesis that God exists helps to solve a serious problem with a powerful epistemological theory seems to lend some plausibility to the claim that God does exist.

THE COHERENCE THEORY OF TRUTH

Hackett defends the coherence theory of truth as a corollary to the epistemological theory which he develops and calls a form of "rational empiricism." Hackett follows Kant in affirming, as a condition of the possibility of knowledge, the necessity of an *a priori* categorical structure which the mind imposes on experience. The coherence theory of truth maintains, according to Hackett,

> that the truth or falsity of any proposition whatever is to be tested and determined by the consideration of: (i) whether or not the proposition results from a self-consistent application of the categorical structure to experimental data; and (ii) whether or not such proposition is systematically correlated both with the data in question and with the whole body of previously established propositions.[2]

I agree with Hackett in his contention that the coherence theory is correct. I shall attempt in this section to further clarify the coherence theory of truth and to show that it entails that the ultimate goal of thought is a perfectly coherent system of knowledge.

The coherence theory of truth is first of all a theory about how rational inquirers do and should test the truth of propositions. To decide whether we should think that a proposition is true, we determine whether it coheres with the body of propositions already believed. If a proposition appears to contradict one that is already believed, then we must either reject that proposition, reject the propositions contradicted by it, or find some way of resolving the apparent contradiction. Propositions which do cohere with the body of beliefs already accepted are regarded as true, and propositions which do not are either rejected or made to fit in by making adjustments in the accepted body of beliefs. We should try to organize the whole body of our beliefs so that they fit together in a coherent system. We attempt to make our thought fully accord with itself, so that all data presented to thought are unified into a self-consistent, comprehensive, and well-ordered system. If we could get all possible experience—sensory, practical, moral, aesthetic, and religious—to cohere perfectly into a system, we would thereby possess the whole truth. The mind would be at one with itself and with reality. The reason that coherence is the criterion by which we determine whether a proposition is true is that the final goal of thought is a perfectly coherent grasp of the whole of reality. When we judge a proposition to be false because it fails to cohere with our present system of beliefs, we are presupposing, in effect, that a belief which fails to cohere with our system would not cohere with a perfectly coherent system, insofar as we take

---

[2]Hackett, *Resurrection*, p. 101.

our present to be an approximation of the perfect system. Thus, taking coherence as a criterion of truth assumes that we want our system to approximate as closely as possible a perfectly coherent system, which is therefore the *telos* towards which thought tends. Implicit in this view is the assumption that a perfectly coherent system would be the whole truth, that it would encompass or represent perfectly the whole of reality.

One of the great proponents of the coherence theory, F. H. Bradley, states the following about the use of coherence as a criterion of truth:

> Facts are justified because, and as far as, while taking them as real, I am better able to deal with the incoming new 'facts' and in general to make my world wider and more harmonious. The higher and wider my structure, and the more that any particular fact or set of facts is implied in that structure, the more certain are the structure and the facts. And if we could reach an all-embracing ordered whole, then our certainty would be absolute. But since we cannot do this, we have to remain content with relative probability.[3]

Bradley emphasizes here that the ultimate goal of thought is an ideal which can never be reached in practice. This is a point of fundamental importance and will be a premise in the subsequent argument connecting the coherence theory of truth to theism. But equally important is the point that even though ideal coherence cannot be reached by finite knowers endowed with discursive intellects, dependent on perspectival experience which is ordered by conceptual frameworks couched in culturally relative thought patterns, still perfect coherence is the ideal against which we evaluate our developing systems of thought.

Thus far we have mentioned consistency and comprehensiveness as marks of coherence. Virtually no one maintains that logical consistency is a sufficient condition of truth, although very few deny that it is a necessary condition. The great proponents of the coherence theory have a much richer notion of coherence than mere logical consistency. Coherence theorists generally include comprehensiveness as an essential component of systematic coherence. Since the absolute system would be one that encompasses the whole of reality, we rank our actually achieved systems according to

---

[3]F.H. Bradley, "On Truth and Coherence," in *Essays in Truth and Reality* (Oxford: The Clarendon Press, 1914), pp. 202-18.

their degree of comprehensiveness, for by this they approximate a characteristic of the ideal. For example, a scientific paradigm is considered superior to its rivals if it explains a broader range of phenomena.

In addition to consistency and comprehensiveness, a coherent system possesses an internal unity and an interconnectedness of its elements. The propositions are logically connected to each other. Most coherence theorists recognize that to demand that each proposition in the system logically entail and be entailed by every other is too stringent. Brand Blanshard argues that in the perfectly coherent system each proposition implies and is implied by every other by bonds of logical necessity, but he then articulates a doctrine of degrees of logical necessity in order to moderate the stringency of the requirement.[4] Parsimony, aesthetic harmony, elegance, and so forth, also constitute norms by which the internal unity of a system is determined. In a coherent system diverse elements are brought into unity, and more parsimonious and elegant theories do this better than their rivals. There seem to be various ways in which the unification within a system is achieved, and it may not be possible to stipulate in advance of inquiry what sorts of unities and relations may emerge as inquiry proceeds. I think that it is part of the task of rational inquiry to discover, and not just stipulate in advance, the precise character of the unity which pervades a coherent system. And to specify a more definite sense of the requirement might prematurely hinder the progress of thought. In any case, further refinement of this aspect of coherence is beyond the scope of this paper and fortunately is not essential to the present purpose.

Implicit in what has just been stated is the point that the coherence theory need not hold that all knowledge is *a priori* or can be deduced logically from a single principle or small number of axioms. The system may be informed by all sorts of *a posteriori* data and may involve a wide variety of kinds of relations to bind together the component parts into a systematically ordered whole. The theory is incompatible with pure empiricism; it denies that a separate perception or cluster of perceptions in isolation from the whole network of experiences and beliefs of a person can justify a truth claim. The epistemic authority of sensory experience is freely admitted, but the data of sense must obtain their epistemic credentials by uniting with the whole body of thought and

---

[4]Brand Blanshard, *The Nature of Thought,* 2 vols. (London: George Allen and Unwin, 1939), 2: 304 and following.

experience already received. The absolute system is not totalitarian, but neither is it radically individualistic.

DEFENSE OF COHERENCE AS THE CRITERION OF TRUTH

A very strong argument in favor of the view that coherence is the criterion of truth is that it can be defended while avoiding the difficulty that haunts arguments for criteria—what Chisholm identifies as the Problem of the Criterion.[5] The problem is that when arguing for a criterion of truth one must, in order to argue consistently with that very criterion, evaluate the truth of the proposition expressing the fact that it is the criterion in terms of that criterion itself. Thus it seems that any argument for a criterion of truth must be question-begging.

The problem of the criterion can be avoided by the argument for coherence. Defending coherence as the criterion of truth is not question-begging inasmuch as there is no alternative to accepting coherence as a criterion of truth.[6] To deny that coherence is a criterion of truth implies incoherence. In order to make an argument for or against any criterion of truth, one must assume the law of non-contradiction. This fact led Bertrand Russell[7] to conclude that coherence is not the ultimate test of truth because coherence depends upon the law of non-contradiction. However, as both Blanshard and Hackett argue, the authority of the law of non-contradiction is based on the fact that thought must be coherent in order to be true.[8] We would have no reason to abide by the law of non-contradiction if coherence were not a requirement and a test of truth. The fact that no proposition can be true unless it coheres with other propositions which are true means that any argument for or against any criterion of truth rests upon coherence as a basic criterion of truth. Without a tacit assumption of coherence as a criterion of truth there would be no intelligible way of distinguishing truth and falsity, and thus the notion of truth would be unintelligible. Any attempt, therefore, to deny

---

[5]Roderick M. Chisholm, *The Problem of the Criterion* (Milwaukee: Marquette University Press, 1973).

[6]For a more extended treatment of the argument developed here, see Robert T. Lehe, "Coherence and the Problem of the Criterion," *Idealistic Studies* (May 1989).

[7]Bertrand Russell, *The Problems of Philosophy* (Oxford: The Clarendon Press, 1912), p. 191.

[8]Hackett, *Resurrection*, p. 103; Blanshard, *Thought*, 2:252-53.

would be contained in the other. So far we would have a contradiction, and until it were resolved, we would not have two comprehensive, coherent systems at all. One of the systems must contain a false proposition, and since a comprehensive system can contain no false propositions, the system containing the false proposition cannot be comprehensive. The system containing the false proposition will lack the truth expressed by the negation of that proposition and so will for this reason be less than comprehensive.

Now any coherence theorist would admit that two *relatively* coherent theories could be in conflict with each other and, therefore, contain false propositions. Such theories are false insofar as they fall short of the ideal of complete systematic coherence. The claim that two equally coherent systems can conflict with each other is no argument against the coherence theory of truth unless it is assumed that the systems are fully coherent. And this assumption is clearly based on the assumption that partial, incomplete systems can be fully coherent. And this assumption presupposes that coherence does not require comprehensiveness. But if coherence does imply comprehensiveness, the objection loses its force.

Any system that falls short of the ideal system which encompasses the whole of reality must be incoherent to some degree, if by coherence we mean a fully comprehensive systematic unity, wherein every proposition is logically connected to every other. Since it is impossible for two conflicting systems to meet this standard of coherence, the claim that this is possible cannot justify the claim that a coherent system might be false. Furthermore, any other attempt to justify the claim that a fully coherent system could be false will inevitably lead to incoherence, since it would have to involve an appeal to a truth outside the system, which cannot possibly exist, since by hypothesis it is the one all-inclusive system which is being considered. Since a fully coherent system must therefore be true, any system which fails to be true must to some degree fail to be coherent. Since there are no systems which are fully coherent and yet false, this objection to the coherence theory of truth thus falls apart.

We have been examining the objection to the coherence theory based on the claim that a fully coherent system could be false since two fully and equally coherent systems could be inconsistent with each other. A somewhat different argument for the claim that a fully coherent system need not be true is based on the correspondence theory of the nature of truth. Since truth is ultimately the correspondence between thought and reality, there is no reason that a fully coherent system of thought must be a perfectly accurate representation of reality. Therefore coherence is not a sufficient criterion of truth.

Hackett's reply to this objection involves his acceptance of what he calls "epistemological dualism."[9] According to that doctrine, the real object of knowledge is numerically distinct from the subjective content of consciousness. Finite minds know reality through the medium of representative ideas which are distinct from the objects known. We never have direct and immediate access to reality, nor is the content of consciousness identical with the objective reality known. This doctrine is one that is clearly assumed by the proponent of the objection under consideration, insofar as it is based on the assumption of the correspondence theory of truth and of a mind-independent reality to which a perfectly coherent thought might fail to correspond. Now Hackett argues that we have direct access only to the contents of consciousness and cannot get outside of our minds to compare our ideas to a thought-independent reality. This premise is used by Blanshard to argue against the correspondence theory of the nature of truth.[10] Blanshard argues that if truth consisted in the correspondence between thought and mind-independent reality, there could be no test of truth, and skepticism would result. Hackett as well as Blanshard argues that skepticism is incoherent. But Hackett accepts the common sense notion that truth consists in the correspondence between thought and reality.[11] The correspondence theory explains what truth is, but not how it is tested. Since we cannot get outside the circle of our ideas, and since skepticism is incoherent, the only way we have of determining the truth of our thought is by the criterion of coherence. Therefore coherence must be a sufficient criterion of truth.

The demand for coherence is internal to the nature of thought itself. The perfectly coherent system is the one which fully meets the demand of thought for a completely unified and ordered synthesis of all material which can be presented to thought. If the goal of thought is a perfectly coherent system, the objection to the coherence theory that a perfectly coherent system might fail to correspond to reality would clearly entail skepticism, for the objection supposes that even when thought is perfectly faithful to

---

[9]Hackett, *Resurrection*, p. 106.

[10]Blanshard, *Thought*, 2:260-66.

[11]Hackett, *Resurrection*, p. 104.

its own demands, it might fail to faithfully represent reality. This supposition rests upon a conception of a split between thought and reality which could not in principle be overcome by any feat of cognitive acrobatics. The implication of such a conception is the impossibility of knowledge.

Now the objector might reply that the argument just given begs the question inasmuch as it assumes that coherence is the goal of thought, whereas in fact, correspondence to reality is the goal of thought. Actually, the coherence theory claims that the goal of thought is a perfectly coherent system, which is that system which perfectly represents reality. Since on all sides it is admitted that a perfectly coherent system cannot actually be achieved, the objector cannot show that such a system does fail to correspond to reality by comparing the system with reality apprehended through some other medium. The objector would have support for his position if he could produce an instance where a proposition which cohered less well with the accepted belief system than a competitor were nevertheless found more likely to be true. I do not see any way of justifying such a proposition without in some way or another involving an appeal to the coherence of the proposition with other beliefs or empirical data. Even an appeal to direct intuition or mystical insight would ultimately involve relating such experience to other sources of belief. To accept them as sources of knowledge would require at least the coherence of the belief that they are sources of knowledge with the rest of one's belief system. Of course, one can live with unresolved contradictions and "cognitive dissonance." But as long as one does, one's system falls short of coherence and is insofar untrue. In the end we have no source of knowledge that does not involve the incorporation of beliefs into the whole web of accepted beliefs. Therefore, I do not see how any reasonable case can be made for the claim that coherence is not a sufficient criterion of truth or that a perfectly coherent system could fail to correspond to reality.

THE UNATTAINABILITY OF THE
IDEAL SYSTEM AND THE REALITY OF GOD

One final objection to the coherence theory is that the perfectly coherent system is impossible to realize or even conceive and cannot therefore serve as a regulative guide to theoretical inquiry. Since the ideal is impossible to conceive, we can never know whether our present working system does cohere with the ideal system, and so the coherence theory offers no useful criterion by which to test the truth of our beliefs. According to Michael Williams, the coherence theory of truth gives us ". . . no reason to think that a judgment's fitting in with our system of present knowledge tells us anything about its relations to a completed system."[12] Williams further alleges that "we have no idea what it would be for a theory to be ideally complete and comprehensive in the way required for coherence theories of truth, or what it would be for inquiry to have an end. Nor do we need the concept of an ideal theory to make sense of the idea that knowledge progresses."[13]

Now what about the claim that the idea of a complete and comprehensive system is unnecessary in order to conceive of the progress of inquiry? Williams says that we understand the progress of knowledge "retrospectively by seeing how a later view improves over its predecessors. We do not have to rely on the notion of a perfected view towards which inquiry is progressing."[14] Unfortunately we do have to have some idea of the end of inquiry in order that our retrospective vision perceive genuine progress and not mere change. If we see that our present theories are more unified, consistent, and comprehensive than their predecessors, and if we regard this as a mark of superiority and not a mere difference, it is precisely because they have been evaluated in light of the ideal of systematic coherence as the fundamental normative standard governing inquiry. We recognize a theory as superior to a predecessor if it is more consistent, more comprehensive, more parsimonious, and so forth. And to that extent we recognize progress by looking back. But we recognize increased consistency, comprehensiveness and systematic unity as marks of progress only because a system that more closely approximates the ideal of a complete and fully comprehensive system is superior to one which is farther from that ideal. The details of such a system are unknown to us from our present, and any future, point of view. And typically investigators do not go about with a fully articulated, explicit conception of the idea of system at the surface of their consciousness. But the idea of the goal of thought is nevertheless implicitly assumed in any rational assessment of the progress achieved at

---

[12]Michael Williams, "Coherence, Justification, and Truth," *Review of Metaphysics* 37 (1980):243-72.

[13]Ibid.

[14]Ibid.

any point. One does not need a clear conception of the ultimate goal of thought or even to believe there is one in order to do scientific research or to think rationally. But any rational assessment of the progress of inquiry logically presupposes the idea of the end toward which inquiry tends, whether or not one explicitly acknowledges coherence as that end. Apart from the idea of such a goal, the idea of progress is unintelligible.

Is it true that the coherence theory of truth gives no reason "to think that a judgment's fitting in with our system of present knowledge tells us anything about its relations to a completed system?" It is a very common criticism of the coherence theory that since the absolute system is an unattainable ideal, there is no way to know whether anything that we believe now coheres with the absolute system. This criticism is in part true and in part based on a misunderstanding of the coherence theory. The truth in the criticism is that we, indeed, never can be absolutely sure that any particular belief will continue to be held as inquiry progresses. This, however, is not so much a criticism uniquely applicable to the coherence theory as it is a recognition of the fallibility of our knowledge. The misunderstanding upon which the criticism is based concerns the relation between the ideal system and the partial systems actually achieved. Although the complete embodiment of the absolute system is an unrealizable goal, the system is not alien to our achieved fruits of inquiry. The fact that I can never have the absolute system means that I cannot be absolutely sure that my present system will continue to hold up as inquiry progresses. To the extent that I am justified in thinking that my present system is adequate, I am justified in thinking that it will hold up or that it will require only minor modification. As a system maintains its integrity through continued investigation, we become relatively more certain of its adequacy. It seems quite reasonable to say that the degree of our justification that our system is adequate is just the degree of the probability of its remaining intact as inquiry progresses toward its goal. In other words, the degree of our justification for a system is the degree to which we are justified in thinking that it approximates the ideal system. There is no justification for the claim that all our beliefs might be false or that our present working theories are totally incoherent. But this means that our present knowledge does to some degree cohere with the absolute system. It is incoherent to say, "I know that my present system is fairly coherent, but I can never know whether it would hold in comparison to the absolute system, since the latter is forever beyond my reach." For a partial system to be coherent at all just means that it is coherent with the absolute system—to some degree. According to the coherence theory, any partial realization of systematic coherence is a partial realization of the absolute system. Partially coherent means an approximation of perfect coherence. If a belief seems to fit in with our present, relatively coherent system of knowledge, the likelihood that it coheres with the ideal system is determined by the likelihood that it really does fit in with our present system and by the degree to which our present system really is coherent—which is exactly the degree to which it coheres with the ideal system.

The objections raised by Williams, therefore, can be answered. We do in fact need an ideal of perfect coherence in order to make sense of how coherence can be a criterion of truth and in order to evaluate the degree to which actual systems approximate the final truth. Furthermore, the impossibility of our realizing a perfectly coherent system does not make it impossible to use the ideal as a regulative principle by which to guide inquiry. However, the unrealizability of the absolute system does still pose a difficulty for the coherence theory.

In order for the absolute system to constitute the *telos* and regulative guide of inquiry, it must in some sense really exist as a possible object of thought. Our idea of the system is indeterminate and indefinite. But there must be an absolute system which is fully determinate—otherwise no partial system can be an approximation of an absolute system. If human beings are incapable of conceiving in a fully determinate way the absolute system, and if coherence is the criterion of truth, then there must be some way of accounting for the reality of the system other than through the actual or possible realization of it by human minds. The problem is solved if we hypothesize the existence of an omniscient Mind which does comprehend the whole of reality in a perfectly coherent knowledge. We can account for the possibility of the actuality of the absolute system if we postulate the existence of God. If the postulation of God's existence explains how a perfectly coherent system is possible and actual, and can explain how our limited system can be guided by an ideal of absolute coherence, then this constitutes a strong argument in favor of the reality of God.

But perhaps the problem of the unrealizability of the perfect system can be more forcefully pressed by arguing that the perfect system is not merely beyond the possibility of human attainment, but is in principle absolutely impossible. Perhaps it is in the very nature of coherent systems that they cannot possibly be comprehensive or ideally coherent in the sense demanded by the coherence theory of truth. Then it would seem that the very notion of a perfectly coherent system would be unintelligible, and therefore could not function as a normative standard by which to evaluate the results of inquiry or as the basis of an argument for the existence of God.

This suggestion requires us to look more closely at the way in which the coherence of actual cognitive systems is limited. It is not just that human beings, being finite, are capable of acquiring only a finite number of facts, whereas the total system includes all the facts. If that were the only sense in which the perfect system is impossible, then such impossibility would pose no special problem for the coherence theory. The total system would be the system which incorporated the totality of the facts, and we are capable only of knowing a limited number of those facts. But we could easily conceive the ideal of a system which incorporates all the facts, and so there is no threat to the coherence theory posed by the impossibility of our knowing all the facts. The problem for the coherence theory, unfortunately, is much more serious.

Recent work in epistemology and the philosophy of science—from several philosophical traditions: phenomenology, hermeneutics, and analytic philosophy[15] —has produced a conception of knowledge and rationality that entails a much more radical sort of alienation of human thought from an ideal of perfect coherence. Much of this work, in particular that of such philosophers as Kuhn, Feyerabend, Goodman, Lehrer, Quine, and Rorty,[16] has been congenial to coherentism in a broad sense, but very hostile to the idea of a perfectly coherent system as the goal of rational inquiry. It is held that thought always takes place within the context of a more or less coherent system, or conceptual framework. Beliefs are justified by their fittedness to the accepted framework. The problem is that the framework colors the way the facts are

---

[15]See Richard Bernstein, *Beyond Objectivism and Relativism* (Philadelphia: University of Pennsylvania Press, 1983); Michael Krausz and Jack W. Meiland, eds., *Relativism—Cognitive and Moral* (Notre Dame: University of Notre Dame Press, 1982); Martin Hollis and Steve Lukas, eds., *Rationality and Relativism* (Cambridge: The MIT Press, 1984).

[16]See T.S. Kuhn, *The Structure of Scientific Revolutions* (Chicago: University of Chicago Press, 1975); Nelson Goodman, *Ways of Worldmaking* (Indianapolis: Hackett Publishing Co., 1978); Keith Lehrer, *Knowledge* (Oxford and New York: Oxford University Press, 1974); W.V.O. Quine, *Ontological Relativity and Other Essays* (New York: Columbia University Press, 1969); Richard Rorty, "The World Well Lost," *Journal of Philosophy* 69 (1972):649-66 and *Philosophy and the Mirror of Nature* (Princeton: Princeton University Press, 1979).

represented and interpreted. Alternative frameworks are possible and may be incommensurable with each other. Beliefs which are justified in one framework may not be even expressible (without at least some loss of meaning) in the terms available to an alternative framework. Furthermore, the construction of the framework itself is determined in large measure by non-rational, historical, and cultural factors of which thinkers operating within the framework are scarcely aware. There is no independent standpoint by which to judge one framework superior to others, and no one categorical scheme can be regarded as unique. Accordingly, it turns out that because of the nature of conceptual systems, no system can, in principle, be comprehensive in the sense demanded by the coherence theory of truth or be regarded as an approximation of ultimate truth. The deficiency of the kind of conceptual systems which we possess is incurable, and the resources for a possible cure are not within our cognitive grasp. Therefore, no system possible for a human mind can present more than a partial, fragmentary, and perspectival version of reality. This would seem to imply that the idea of an absolutely coherent and comprehensive system is anathema to human understanding, in a way that dooms the prospect of evaluating cognitive systems in light of the ideal of absolute coherence. We have argued, however, that coherence is the ultimate criterion of truth and that the application of this criterion does involve the idea of an absolutely coherent system. We seem to be caught in a stultifying predicament unless some way can be found of making sense of the possibility of absolute coherence.

An unmitigated version of this kind of coherentism, which denies the possibility of an ideal system, clearly entails epistemological relativism. Such a view in the end entails the impossibility of knowledge and is therefore incoherent. If all beliefs must be justified by their coherence with a system, but if no conceptual system can itself be justified in terms of coherence with an ideal system which encompasses the whole truth, then the relation of any finite system to reality is forever unknowable. It seems that coherentism without an ideal system entails the impossibility of genuine knowledge. But such a view can be taken seriously only if it could itself possibly be justified as true in a sense which the view itself implies is impossible. A view which implies the impossibility of knowledge cannot be asserted as true without undercutting what the view maintains. This relativistic coherentism is therefore self-referentially incoherent.

We can still admit much of what philosophers like Goodman and Rorty say about the relativity of conceptual systems which human beings are capable of constructing. If the limitations of the conceptual systems of which finite minds are capable are indeed impossible for human beings to overcome, this does not negate the possibility of the reality of an absolute Mind not subject to these limitations. We can admit the limitations of our own systems without admitting that these limitations attend to the knowledge possessed by an infinite Mind. In fact, the sort of coherentism which insists upon the relativity and incommensurability of systems only intensifies the need for a way of accounting for the intelligibility of the ideal of an absolute system to which our incomplete system can bear some relation. Coherentism would imply skepticism were it not that, despite the fact that human thought is limited in a way that makes an ideally coherent system in principle beyond human attainment, we can conceive the idea of a perfectly coherent system as the possession of an absolute, unlimited, omniscient Mind.

The best humanly possible scientific theory or theoretical system is still only a limited, perspectival version of reality. And so we will never reach, nor can we conceive in detail what it would mean to have, a perfectly coherent system. The idea of the absolute system is for us indeterminate, insofar as we are incapable of rendering our thought absolutely coherent. But the idea of an absolutely coherent grasp of the whole of reality is not unintelligible because we can conceive the idea of an omniscient Mind, whose thought is perfectly coherent and does thereby agree perfectly with the whole of reality. Thus the idea of God makes it possible to conceive the idea of a perfect and unlimited intellect, whose thought is absolutely true—fully coherent with itself and with reality. The idea of God helps us to make sense of how our finite understanding can be thought of as an approximation of ideal coherence and of how human knowledge is indeed genuine knowledge, even though it is rooted in systems which can never be perfectly coherent. Our imperfect systems embody knowledge which can be thought of as approximating the perfectly coherent knowledge possessed by God. We cannot, of course, see in detail how our thought resembles God's, inasmuch as God's mind is beyond our comprehension. But we can at least conceive the possibility that the application of the canons of rationality which we employ in working out our theories and systems does lead us to some approximation of ultimate truth. The hypothesis of the existence of God is not intended as a way of making it easier to compare our limited systems with the absolute system, but rather to make it intelligible how there could be an absolute system and how our systems could in principle be rationally thought to approximate an absolute system.

It might be objected that this argument does not entail the actual existence of God, but only the idea of God as a heuristic fiction. We need the idea of God to render intelligible the notion of a perfectly coherent system. This is an important objection and raises the very difficult issue of whether an idea which is necessary for the coherence of our thought and which refers to a transcendent object corresponds to an object which actually exists. This is the problem which concerned Kant in the "Dialectic" of the *Critique of Pure Reason,* and this is not the place to rewrite that work. It is worth pointing out, however, that the objection under consideration seems to rest upon a split between thought and reality which threatens the possibility of genuine knowledge of reality. Hackett is among the large number of philosophers who argue persuasively against Kant's refusal to countenance the application of our concepts to reality as it is in itself. If the idea of God, as it functions in the coherence theory to make intelligible the idea of a perfectly coherent system, were only a heuristic fiction, I do not see that it would provide an escape from the skeptical implications of coherentism devoid of an absolute system. For coherentism to avoid skepticism, it is not only necessary that we have an *idea* of an absolute system, but there must actually *be* an absolute system of which our present systems actually are approximations. If there is not actually a Mind that possesses the perfectly coherent system, then there really is no such system. And if there is no such system then in no sense is a relatively coherent system an approximation of it. So if God did not exist, we would have no criterion of truth, and the impossibility of knowledge would result.

Considered merely as an idea, the idea of God is no more useful in making intelligible the ideal of perfect coherence than is the idea of the absolute system. But we need more than the intelligibility of an idea. If coherence is the criterion of *truth,* then there must be some ontological ground of the unity of thought and reality that makes it possible that as thought becomes more coherent—as it fulfills its own internal requirements—it at the same time realizes a closer approximation of reality. The concept of God considered merely as a regulative idea may guide the quest for greater coherence, but it does not explain why the termination of that quest (if it could be carried out) would result in knowledge of reality. It is true that the denial that it would is tantamount to skepticism and thus leads to incoherence. This means that we cannot reasonably deny that the coherent system does truly represent reality. But this anti-skeptical argument by itself is not sufficient to explain *why* a coherent system must be true. On the other hand, if we postulate the actual existence of God, an explanation is possible. If God is the ground of all that exists, including thought, and if finite rational minds resemble in a limited way the infinite intelligence of God, then we have the basis of a plausible explanation for the unity of thought and being which makes it possible for coherence to be a criterion of truth.

Even if one is reluctant to accept the proposition that the denial of God's existence entails the impossibility of knowledge, a somewhat more modest argument can be given which might have greater plausibility. Surely the view that God exists, that He comprehends with a perfectly coherent insight the whole of reality, that reality itself conforms to its representation by God's perfectly coherent knowledge, is one which adds systematic coherence to our conception of human understanding and its relation to ultimate truth. If it is supposed that God does not exist, it is, at the very least, more difficult to explain how coherence could be a criterion of truth—how the relative coherence of a cognitive system can rationally justify the presumption of some degree of correspondence to a mind-independent reality. If it is supposed that God does not exist, it is more difficult to explain the rationality of preferring a theory which is more coherent, more parsimonious, more unified than its rivals. On the assumption of atheism, it is more difficult to conceive the relation of our actual conceptual systems to an ideal standard by which they are evaluated. Theism, on the other hand, enables us to make sense of the idea of a perfectly coherent system which encompasses the whole of reality, despite the limitations of our own form of understanding. Theism helps us to make sense of a parallel between thought and being that explains why a coherent system can be rationally thought to correspond to reality and to make sense of a relation between our own finite understanding and a perfectly coherent knowledge of the whole of reality. If God is both the source of the whole of reality and the possessor of a perfectly coherent knowledge of the whole of reality, then it makes sense that there should be a correlation between the order of thought and the structure of being which permits the possibility of knowledge. If that same God is also the source of our own cognitivity, then it is plausible to suppose that the structure of our thought is such that the partial coherence which we achieve when adhering to the canons of our own finite rationality should to some degree reflect or approximate, in a way appropriate to the sort of beings we are, the infinite understanding of God. In short, the hypothesis that God exists renders more coherent our understanding of ourselves as rational beings and the relation of our thought to ultimate reality. Therefore, theism coheres better than does atheism with the rational demand for systematic unity. And in the context of the coherence theory of truth this constitutes a strong reason to favor theism. In this version of the argument, the conclusion is not that the existence of God is necessary in order to explain how coherence can be the criterion of truth, but more modestly, that theism provides a plausible explanation of how coherence can be the criterion of truth and of why it is reasonable to think that human knowledge approximates an ideal of perfect systematic coherence. The idea of God seems useful in order to make sense of the idea of a perfectly coherent system, and the actual existence of God seems to provide a more plausible explanation than does the view that God is merely a regulative idea of the unity of thought and being which is necessary in order for coherence to be the criterion of truth. This does not prove that God exists, but it does constitute an argument for the reasonableness of belief in the existence of God and of the importance of theism for an account of the possibility of knowledge.

Bernard Lonergan has stated that all arguments for the existence of God ". . . are included in the following general form. If the real is completely intelligible, God exists. But the real is completely intelligible. Therefore, God exists."[17] The argument presented in this paper is an epistemological variation of Lonergan's argument form. The coherence theory of truth is based upon the acknowledgement that knowledge depends upon the complete intelligibility of reality. The argument proceeds from the premise that the possibility of knowledge depends upon the adequacy to reality of a perfectly coherent system of thought. The argument then suggests that the existence of the God who is the source of reality and the capacity to know reality is the best explanation of the unity of thought and reality which makes knowledge possible.

A continuation of the project to explore the implications of this coherence theory of truth for the defense of theism might involve the exploration of various ways in which theism contributes to the coherence of our understanding of reality. This is a project in which many philosophers have already extensively engaged. It involves the primarily metaphysical task of developing a theistic worldview. The task of this paper has been to explore the contribution which theism might make to the epistemological

---

[17]Bernard Lonergan, *Insight* (San Francisco: Harper and Row, 1957), p. 672.

task of accounting for the possibility of knowledge and to determine what rational support for theism might be gained in exchange for that contribution.

The Symmetry Of The Past And The Future In The *Kalam* Cosmological Argument

William F. Lawhead

University of Mississippi

In this essay, I wish to expose some puzzles that are created when classical theists use a certain version of the cosmological argument for the existence of God. The argument I have in mind is sometimes called the *kalam* cosmological argument.[1] This argument owes its name to a group of medieval Arabic philosophers who formulated it. This same argument has been used by many Christian theists from Bonaventure up to our contemporaries. For the sake of convenience, I will refer to those who use this argument to prove the existence of God as the "*kalam* apologists."

Briefly, this argument claims that the universe necessarily had a beginning and therefore it must have had a cause. However, it is not obvious that the universe *necessarily* had a beginning, and so this crucial step of the argument needs justification. After all, the great Christian apologist Thomas Aquinas rejected this premise of the *kalam* argument. He thought that it was possible for the universe to have been co-eternal

---

[1]See William Lane Craig, *The* Kalam *Cosmological Argument*, Library of Philosophy and Religion (London: Macmillan, 1979).

with God (even though always dependent upon Him). For Aquinas, it is revelation and not philosophical reason that informs us that the universe had a beginning.[2] Therefore, the heart of the *kalam* argument is another argument that seeks to show that the past is finite. This supporting argument goes like this:

(K1) An actual infinite number of entities cannot exist.

(K2) If the series of past events does not have a beginning, then there exists an actually infinite number of entities.

(K3) Therefore, the series of past events necessarily has a beginning.

The point I wish to establish in this essay is that the *kalam* argument proves too much. If the classical theist uses this argument, it will show not only that the past is finite, but that the future is also. In other words, it forces us to accept a certain modal symmetry between the past and the future. This conclusion unwittingly established by the *kalam* apologist I shall call the "Symmetry Thesis." The Symmetry Thesis can be expressed in two different ways:

(S1) If the series of past events necessarily has a beginning, then the series of future events necessarily has an end.

(S2) If it is possible for the future to be an unending series of events, then it is possible for the past to be a beginningless series of events.

With respect to both propositions, the antecedent is a statement that many classical theists would wish to affirm. However, in each case, the consequent is a statement that most classical theists would not want to affirm.

There are really only two simple propositions that make up the above conditionals. I will examine them in turn. The first proposition is the more controversial of the two.

---

[2]Thomas Aquinas, *Summa Theologica* I, Q. 46, A. 2.

It is the claim that stands at the heart of the *kalam* argument and which we have already labeled (K3):

(K3) The series of past events necessarily has a beginning.

The second proposition is not in dispute. I am not familiar with any philosopher who would doubt the claim that:

(K4) It is possible for the future to be an unending series of events.

In fact, everyone seems to accept the even stronger claim that it is not only possible but actually the case that the future will be an unending series of events. Traditional Christians certainly believe that though the universe as we presently know it may not endure, something will. For example, Thomas Aquinas says, "We do not hold that the world is eternal, nor that generation and movement will go on for ever . . . ."[3] Nevertheless, he says, there will be an infinite series of future events in terms of "the thoughts and affections of hearts, which will be multiplied to infinity since rational creatures will endure forever."[4] However, the thesis of an unending future is not unique to Christians. Even materialists assume that there will always be a future, even if it is only an unending series of physical events.

Notice that in my original two conditionals, propositions (S1) and (S2), the two simple propositions I am now discussing, (K3) and (K4), are in tension with each other. If one is asserted, the other is denied. However, while they are not intrinsically contradictory, I shall attempt to show that they do become incompatible claims within the context of the *kalam* argument and classical theism. Thus, while many classical theists assert (K3) and (K4), other claims they wish to make lead to (S1) and (S2) in which (K3) and (K4) are incompatible.

---

[3]Ibid., I, Q. 14, A. 12.
[4]Ibid.

For now, we need to examine why *kalam* apologists have asserted (K3), the claim that the series of past events necessarily has a beginning. As we saw above, this claim is the conclusion of an argument whose main premise is:

(K1) An actual infinite number of entities cannot exist.

But what reasons could make this premise plausible? The answer that is standardly given is that the negation of this premise would be self-contradictory or absurd. I will analyze this claim by referring to the arguments of two contemporary philosophers of religion, William Lane Craig and Stuart C. Hackett.[5]

Craig presents us with an argument based on "Hilbert's Hotel."[6] This refers to the ideas of the German mathematician David Hilbert. Craig asks us to imagine a hotel with an infinite number of rooms. (It would obviously be an actual infinite.) The rooms are all full. However, when a new guest shows up, the innkeeper makes room for him by shifting the person in room #1 to room #2, the person in room #2 to room #3, and so on. This process is repeated on into infinity. The innkeeper will always be able to find another room, since an infinite series has no limit. Now the new guest can check into room #1 and all the previous guests each have rooms. By means of this process, the hotel could continue to accommodate an unlimited number of new guests, even though all the rooms are full. There are two absurdities here. Originally, all the rooms were full, but because there is no termination point in an infinite series, it appears that new guests could still be added to the series. Second, even with the addition of new guests, there is still the same number of guests now as there was at first. The number of guests is always infinite even though their company is being increased. Concerning this sort of situation, Hackett says it is "self-contradictory since an actually infinite series does not admit of increase or decrease."[7] For this reason Craig asserts, "These

[5]Craig, *Kalam*; Idem, "*Creatio ex nihilo*," in *Process Theology*, ed. Ronald H. Nash (Grand Rapids, MI: Baker Book House, 1987); Stuart C. Hackett, *The Resurrection of Theism* (Chicago: Moody Press, 1957).

[6]Craig, *Kalam*, pp. 84-85; Idem., "*Creatio ex nihilo*," pp. 156-158.

[7]Hackett, *Resurrection*, p. 294.

sorts of absurdities illustrate the impossibility of the existence of an actually infinite number of things."[8]

Similarly, Craig asks us to imagine a library with an infinite number of books in it.[9] Each book is stamped with a unique natural number on it. Now it seems perfectly possible that we can always add one more book to any library. However, if we did that to this library, it would be impossible to number this new book and impossible to count all the books in the library, since all the natural numbers have been used up at the beginning. As Craig concludes, "This is absurd, since entities that exist in reality can be numbered."[10] Once again, when we try to imagine an actual infinite set, we find ourselves imagining an impossible situation.

With this background in place, I am now ready to begin getting to the point of this essay. Classical theists (such as Craig and Hackett) who wish to use these mathematical arguments about infinity to prove the existence of God also want to maintain a kind of modal asymmetry with respect to the past and the future. In other words, they want to say that even though the past is necessarily finite, it is still possible for the future to be an unending series of events. However, I shall argue that on this one point their position leads to a modal symmetry between the past and the future. Hence, propositions (S1) and (S2) are unavoidable. If this is true, it is very ironic. The *kalam* argument provides philosophical justification for the biblical claim that the world had a beginning. However, it also has the unfortunate consequence that, contrary to traditional theology, all future events must have an end. As Aquinas realized, if those who are blessed are going to enjoy eternity worshiping and loving God, then there must be an unending series of events in the future.

I shall briefly set out my argument which shows that the *kalam* argument commits the classical theist to the symmetry of the past and the future. After that, I shall explain and defend its crucial premises. I shall call this argument the neo-*kalam* argument:

(NK1) An actual infinite number of entities cannot exist.

---

[8]Craig, *"Creatio ex nihilo,"* p. 158.

[9]Craig, *Kalam*, pp. 82-84.

[10]Ibid., p. 83.

(NK2) If the series of future events is unending, then there exists an actually infinite number of entities.

(NK3) Therefore, there cannot be an unending series of future events.

Craig, however, has already provided a response to those who assert the claim in (NK2).[11] His reply is based on a crucial distinction that was first set out by Aristotle. This distinction is between an actual infinite (which Craig rejects) and a potential infinite (which Craig accepts). Briefly, we can say that an actual infinite is a completed set which contains an infinite number of members. On the other hand, a potential infinite is a finite collection that continuously grows towards infinity but never reaches its termination point. Craig provides a number of specific, identifying characteristics of each kind of infinity. According to Craig:

1a. An actual infinite is a "completed unity" (quoting mathematician David Hilbert).[12]
1b. By contrast, the potential infinite is never complete. It is always on the way.

2a. An actual infinite is a "determinate" collection of entities.[13]
2b. The potential infinite is an "indefinite collection."[14]

3a. An actual infinite has acquired all the members it is going to have. One cannot add to an actual infinite.[15]

---

[11]In discussing Kant's first antinomy, Craig responds to versions of the Symmetry Thesis proposed by Bertrand Russell, P.J. Zwart, and J.J.C. Smart (*Kalam*, pp. 189-202).

[12]David Hilbert, "On the Infinite," in *Philosophy of Mathematics*, ed. Paul Benacerraf and Hilary Putnam (Englewood Cliffs, NJ: Prentice-Hall, 1964), p. 139. Quoted in Craig, *Kalam*, p. 68.

[13]Ibid., p. 84.
[14]Ibid., p. 97.
[15]Ibid., pp. 83-85.

3b. A potential infinite can always have one more member added to it. "A potential infinite can be increased *limitlessly* . . . ."[16]

4a. The actual infinite is "realized" or "accomplished" (Fernand Van Steenberghen).[17] Since it has achieved completion, it is a static collection.
4b. The potential infinite is always in process and ever increasing.[18] It is something that is "becoming" or "happening" (David Hilbert).[19]

5a. The actual infinite "really is infinite."[20] It is the "true infinite" (Georg Cantor).[21]
5b. The potential infinite is really infinite in name only, for in the truest sense of the word, "the potential infinite at any particular point is always finite."[22]

Using these distinctions, Craig rejects (NK2) and thus tries to avoid the Symmetry Thesis. He claims that a series of events in the past with no beginning would constitute an actual infinite, while an unending future would be merely a potential infinite. Thus, if there really are two kinds of infinite sets, one which characterizes past events and one which characterizes future events, then it is coherent to treat the past and the future differently. As he puts it, "There is no absurdity in holding that the universe began to exist and will continue forever, since at any point the series of events will always be finite and increasing."[23]

---

[16]Ibid., p. 184.

[17]F. Van Steenberghen, 'Le "processus in infinitum" dans les trois première "voies" de saint Thomas,' *Revista Portuguesa de Filosofia* 30 (1974): 128. Quoted in Craig, *Kalam*, p. 96.

[18]Ibid., p. 97.

[19]Hilbert, "Infinite," p. 139. Quoted in Craig, *Kalam*, p. 67.

[20]Craig, *"Creatio ex nihilo,"* p. 156.

[21]Ibid., p. 67.

[22]Ibid., p. 66.

[23]Ibid., p. 197.

In spite of this argument, however, I do not think that Craig can dismiss (NK2) that easily. Therefore, I offer the following argument to support that premise of the neo-*kalam* argument. I will call it the neo-*kalam* supplement:

(NKS1) The series of future events is unending.
[Working Premise]

(NKS2) God has perfect knowledge of all future events.
[The Foreknowledge Thesis of Classical Theism]

(NKS3) The set of future events contained within God's knowledge constitutes
a determinate, complete, actually infinite set.
[Inference from (NKS1), (NKS2)]

(NK2) Therefore, if the series of future events is unending, then there exists an
actually infinite number of entities.
[Inference from (NKS1), (NKS3)]

The addition of (NKS2), which I shall call the Foreknowledge Thesis, unravels Craig's defense. As was noted, this premise is a standard doctrine within classical theism and is one that Craig accepts.[24] What may not yet be clear is the inference to (NKS3). I shall grant the fact that since future events have not yet occurred, then this set of events is merely a potential infinite. However, if God knows each one of these events that will occur, then the items of knowledge within God's mind constitute an actual infinite set. It is important to keep this distinction in mind throughout the remaining discussion. The future events as-actual-occurrences are a potential infinite, but the future events as-items-of-knowledge in God's mind are an actual infinite. Hence, it is ambiguous to state that "In no sense does the future actually exist."[25] True, it does not exist as a set of actual occurrences. However, it does exist as a closed, determinate set of divine mental contents. It will be revealing to compare the consequences of the

---

[24]William Lane Craig, *The Only Wise God: The Compatibility of Divine Foreknowledge and Human Freedom* (Grand Rapids, MI: Baker Book House, 1987).

[25]Craig, *Kalam*, p. 97.

Foreknowledge Thesis with the previous list of characteristics of actual versus potential infinites that Craig provided for us. I shall include with each remark the number on the previous list to which it refers.

First, if God's knowledge ecompasses the whole of the future, then for God, the future is a completed unity (1a). Second, it would seem that the set of events which will occur in the future makes up a determinate collection. Craig insists that each and every future-tense statement is either true or false.[26] Thus, unlike a potential infinite, which is always indefinite and in the process of being formed (2b), the set of future events known by God is a clearly defined set (2a). Only if the membership of this set were clearly established could any and all statements about the future have truth value in the present. Third, if God knows perfectly every detail of the future, then there are no further possible details that can be added to this picture. No further members can be added to this set (3a). Fourth, for God, the set of all temporal events is eternally foreknown and, hence, it is a static series (4a). As time progresses, various members of this set change their "name tags" from "future" to "present" to "past." However, though their temporal modality may change, neither their number nor their descriptions ever change. Fifth, God's knowledge of future events, then, is a true infinite (5a). From our perspective, the set of future events may be indefinite and open, and in the process of becoming definite and actual. It should be obvious by now, however, that for the perfect knower the set of future events has all the characteristics of an actual infinite.

If future events constitute an infinite set in the mind of God, then this set has the same mathematical characteristics as does the infinite past. It is these same mathematical characteristics that cause the *kalam* apologist to reject the possibility of an infinite past. In a very revealing passage, Craig argues against Aquinas, who suggested that since the past does not exist, the set of past events would be a potential infinite but not an actual infinite. Craig replies:

> The fact that the events do not exist simultaneously is wholly irrelevant to the issue at hand; the fact remains that since past events, as determinate parts of reality, are definite and distinct and can be numbered, they can be conceptually

---

[26]Craig, *Only Wise God*, pp. 55-60.

collected into a totality. Therefore, if the temporal sequence of events is infinite, the set of all past events will be an actual infinite.[27]

It seems perfectly obvious to me that this same argument applies to the future as known by God. Future events are "determinate," "definite," and "distinct." They would have to have these characteristics if Craig is going to maintain that any statement about the future is presently either true or false. Furthermore, if these events can be known, then they can be numbered. Certainly, the Foreknowledge Thesis implies that future events in God's mind are a conceptual totality. It would seem to follow inescapably from Craig's own argument that if the series of future events is endless and thus infinite, then it really is an actual infinite.

In all respects, therefore, the set of future events *as known by God* has all the traits of an actual infinite and none of the traits of a potential infinite. It is only from the standpoint of our human ignorance that the future is "an indefinite collection of events."[28] To speak of the future as merely a potential infinite is to speak from an anthropocentric, phenomenal perspective. It does not correctly characterize reality-as-it-really-is, which surely is identical with reality-as-viewed-by-God.

Once this last point has been understood, then it is clear that the same absurdities Craig claims for an infinite past spring up when we look at the infinite future as embraced by God's foreknowledge. I shall just give a few examples and allow the reader to work out the rest. First, if we were to consider all of the events which are known by God from the year 2500 A.D. on into the endless future, how many would there be?[29] Since the future is unending, the number of events in this set would be infinite. Now then, how many events are there that are items of knowledge within God's mind from the year 2000 A.D. on into the future? There would also be an infinite number within the mind of God. So now we have added 500 years of events to an already infinite sum and have ended up with the same result: infinity. We can say the

---

[27]Craig, *Kalam*, p. 96.

[28]Ibid., p. 97.

[29]Since the figures used are arbitrary, allow me to assume that the universe and, hence, our method of time measurement will last that long.

same thing about this as Stuart Hackett says about the similar situation with respect to the past. "This is self-contradictory since an actually infinite series does not admit of increase or decrease."[30] Similarly, Craig says that we cannot take an actual infinite and add to it.[31]

Another way to describe the problem is this way. God's mind is Hilbert's Hotel. For each numbered room in the hotel, there corresponds a future event in God's mind. Simply rerun all the absurdities with the infinite rooms in the hotel and one will find that they can just as easily be applied to the infinite events in God's foreknowledge. Again, imagine that for each future event recorded in God's foreknowledge, there is a book in the library corresponding to it. The same problems that were noted with the infinite number of books will arise with the thoughts that correspond to them. Two books plus two books equal four books. Two mental contents plus two mental contents equal four. An infinite number of rooms equals an infinite number of books equals an infinite number of mental contents. The mathematics will always be the same.

A *kalam* apologist could seek to evade the force of my argument by claiming that there is a difference between an infinite set which exists in the mind and an actual infinite set that exists in reality. For example, Craig continually insists that Georg Cantor's theory of transfinite numbers is legitimate, because in this domain the infinite is only a theoretical, mental construct. On the other hand, infinite hotel rooms, infinite books in the library, or an infinity of past events is another matter altogether. Anything of this sort would be an actual infinite, and, hence, it would be absurd to say that it could really exist.

I agree with his assessment of Cantor's ideas. As mathematician David Hilbert says, the infinite in Cantor's theory is "nowhere to be found in reality."[32] In other words, it is a kind of mental fiction. I would go even further and say that the infinite cannot even be found within Cantor's mind. It is obvious that Cantor has never held an infinite collection of numbers in his mind in the same sense that we can think of three things or imaginatively picture three objects. Instead, he has come up with various symbols or class names which stand in the place of different sets of infinite objects. He has conceptually "pointed" to the infinite but has never embraced it. By using these class

---

[30]Hackett, *Theism*, p. 294.

[31]Craig, *Kalam*, p. 85.

[32]Hilbert, "Infinite," p. 151. Quoted in Craig, *Kalam*, p. 87.

names in propositions and by formally manipulating his symbols, he has been able to prove various theorems about infinite sets.[33] Hackett comes to terms with this issue by insisting that all mathematical infinites are really potential infinites. As he puts it, "The so-called infinite series in mathematics is not a series that is *actually* infinite in the sense of existence; it merely approaches infinity by reason of the fact that no definite limits are assigned to the series."[34]

While this approach resolves the paradoxes of infinity in mathematics, it does not resolve the paradoxes of infinity in classical theism. In contrast to the above, if God has perfect foreknowledge, He does not just refer to the future with symbols as I do or as Cantor does when he refers to an infinite set. Instead, God's knowledge embraces, in all their rich detail and infinite number, each and every future event. This infinite set is fully actual in the mind of God in a way that the infinite is not actual in a mathematician's mind. What Craig does not realize is that when we have a completed, actual infinite set of entities, the mathematics of this collection remains the same, no matter what the entities are made of. If the set consists of either hotel rooms, library books, past events, or the mental contents of God's mind, their mathematical properties remain the same. After all, since when does mathematics depend upon the composition of those things which we are counting?

In discussing Hilbert's Hotel, Craig says that "These paradoxical results can be avoided only if such actually infinite collections can exist only in the imagination, not in reality."[35] But I do not think that this distinction between what can exist in the imagination and what can exist in reality is relevant here. Craig says that the infamous hotel cannot exist in reality. How does he know this? Did he try to build one with bricks and mortar? No, of course not. His arguments are based on thought experiments which

---

[33]Craig quotes Pamela Huby who makes a similar point:
"It is often said that Cantor legitimized the notion of the actual infinite, and it is well to get clear what this means. What it seems to mean is that we can make statements, within a certain conventional system, about *all* the members of an infinite class, and that we can clearly identify certain classes which have an infinite number of members, and even say, using new conventions, what the cardinal number of their members is. But beyond that Cantor tells us nothing about actual infinity" (Pamela M. Huby, "Kant or Cantor? That the Universe, if Real Must Be Finite in Both Space and Time," *Philosophy* 46 [1971]: 130). Quoted in Craig, *Kalam*, p. 71.

[34]Hackett, *Theism*, p. 294.

[35]Craig, *"Creatio ex nihilo,"* p. 161.

show our inability to imagine such a hotel without leading to absurdities. Thus, the hotel cannot even exist in the imagination except as a name and an abstract description. We can no more imagine such a hotel than we can a round square. It is because the hotel cannot be conceived without contradiction that we conclude that it cannot be built either. It does not matter whether the infinite collection is located in the mind (the imagined hotel or the foreknown future) or is actualized in space and time (the series of past events); the problems with infinite numbers is the same. If Plato was right and numbers are real objects, then we would have the same problems with Cantor's mathematics. However, most mathematicians are not Platonists. Therefore, as it is commonly conceived, the infinite series of natural numbers is not real in the sense that the set of God's thoughts is real.

Allow me to summarize what has been accomplished in this essay. The *kalam* argument shows that the series of past events necessarily has a beginning. But, if we embrace the Foreknowledge Thesis, then my neo-*kalam* argument shows that the series of future events must be finite also. On the other hand, if we insist that it is possible for the future to be unending, then we have to grant the same privilege to the past and admit the possibility of an actual infinite. Hence, I have defended my claim that the *kalam* argument (plus the Foreknowledge Thesis) leads to the Symmetry Thesis.

A careful reader of my argument will recognize that one could use the *kalam* argument to prove the existence of God, but avoid the neo-*kalam* conclusion by rejecting one of its crucial premises, namely, the Foreknowledge Thesis. However, this would mean that one could not use the *kalam* argument to prove the existence of the God of classical theology. It has not been the purpose of this essay to claim either that an actual infinite is possible, divine foreknowledge is impossible, the future is finite, or that the past is infinite. But I think that my arguments do show that it is incoherent for the classical theist to deny all four of these propositions and to assert all their contradictories. If one denies any one of the above statements, then he must accept at least one of the others. In this sort of situation, philosophy makes our choices clear, but it does not make our choices for us. What I have shown is that our choices may be harder than it has been supposed.

Classical Theism And The *Kalam* Principle

Robert Prevost

University of Texas at Arlington

I met Stuart Hackett while I was a student at Trinity Evangelical Divinity School, and I shall never forget studying under him. He was my first contact with real, honest-to-goodness philosophical Idealism. And though that was impressive in itself, it was not the most significant thing about him. Hackett strove to live in a way adequate both to philosophy and to Christianity. And he succeeded. He demonstrated by his own experience that one need not give up a keen analytical mind if one is to remain a faithful Christian. Such a role model was invaluable to this young philosopher as I entered the world of scholarship.

In this essay I want to discuss one element of Hackett's philosophical worldview and its significance for the debate over God's relationship to time. Typically God is described as eternal, as being outside of time. And while it does seem that both tradition and the average Christian believer accept it, this view, call it "classical theism," has received extensive criticism in recent philosophy of religion. The claim that God is unchanging, immutable, and outside of time, it is asserted, is incoherent. If as revealed in Scripture, God loves, creates, and redeems, then God is involved in the world. This involvement, it is argued further, requires that God is in time, that is, that God is everlasting, not eternal. Thus, if by "God" is meant creator and redeemer, one cannot affirm both that God creates and is eternal. Only if time is part of God's being can God be a creator and redeemer.

The battle is usually waged between the Thomists, who hoist the banner of the classical concept, and the personalists, who bear the herald of the modern concept.[1] But there is a third way. Hackett also asserts that God is unchanging and eternal, but not for Thomistic reasons. Hackett accepts the *kalam* principle, which states that an actual infinity is impossible.[2] If God were in time, such an actual infinite would exist. Thus, God must be eternal, outside of time.

I shall argue, *pace* Hackett, that the *kalam* principle does not provide support for the classical concept of God. The argument I shall give will be based on the practical impossibility of determining the truth of the *kalam* principle. Thus, though I can admit that the *kalam* principle may be true, it is not a principle which we can know.

In the first section, I shall place the principle into the context of the contemporary debate over the concept of God. In the second section, I shall examine a recent attempt to say that God is both eternal and temporal. In the third and fourth sections I shall

---

[1]Naturally enough the classical concept can be traced to St. Thomas. See *Summa Theologica* Q. II-XI. One might also look at H.P. Owen, *Concepts of Deity* (London: Macmillan, 1970); E.L. Mascall, *He Who Is* (New York: Longman, Green and Co., 1943); and Brian Davies, *Introduction to Philosophy of Religion* (Oxford: Oxford University Press, 1982) as more contemporary expressions of the classical concept from the Thomistic perspective. The modern, or personalist, concept is represented by, among others, Nicholas Wolterstorff, "God as Everlasting" in *Contemporary Philosophy of Religion*, ed. Steven M. Cahn and David Shatz (New York: Oxford University Press, 1982), pp. 77-98; Richard Swinburne, *The Coherence of Theism* (New York: Oxford University Press, 1977); and Keith Ward, *Rational Theology and the Creativity of God* (Oxford: Blackwell's, 1982).

Though one might consider concepts of God in process theology as modern concepts, I refrain from including them in my description here since they are associated with Whiteheadian metaphysics. Perhaps process concepts of God are yet a fourth source of God concepts available today. If so, they would be closer to the personalist model which I discuss than to the classical concept which it is intended to replace. Cf. Schubert Ogden, "The Reality of God," *The Reality of God and Other Essays* (London: SCM, 1967), pp. 1-70.

[2]I was introduced to the Islamic heritage of this principle by William Lane Craig, *The* Kalam *Cosmological Argument*, Library of Philosophy and Religion (London: Macmillan, 1979). The *kalam* argument found its strongest articulation among the Muslim philosophers of the ninth to twelfth centuries. It is from their

show why the *kalam* principle cannot be used to support the classical concept. In the final section I shall suggest a reason why a theist should reject the *kalam* principle.

I

The classical concept of God is usually associated with St. Thomas. St. Thomas took up Aristotle's concepts of actuality and potentiality as the basic categories of his metaphysics.[3] He conceives God as being pure actuality, Being without a hint of potentiality. Since change requires having the potential to change, God cannot change. And since time is the measurement of change, then God cannot be in time.[4]

Personalism rejects the Thomistic categories and the concept of God identified with it. The central concept on this construal is the concept of a person. God, as illustrated by Richard Swinburne's description, is "a person without a body (*i.e.*, a spirit)."[5] The conclusion follows that God must be in time, or that time must be a property of God, since activity entails a moment before one acts and a moment after one acts. Further, it is argued, if God is omniscient, then He must be in time, since knowledge of what time it is requires a temporal perspective.[6]

The contrast between these two concepts of God serves as a tool for explicating the *kalam* principle. The principle states that an infinity of things cannot exist in actuality. That is to say, there can be no infinite number of things, be it moments of time or material objects. No matter how large the number of things in the universe is, it must contain a finite number of things.

---

discussion that I take the term "*kalam*" to designate the principle. Among contemporary proponents of the *kalam* argument, besides Craig, is, of course, Stuart Hackett, *The Resurrection of Theism,* 2d ed. (Grand Rapids, MI: Baker, 1982) and *The Reconstruction of the Christian Revelation Claim* (Grand Rapids, MI: Baker, 1984).

[3] See Frederick Copleston's discussion of St. Thomas's relationship to Aristotle in his *A History of Philosophy*, 9 vols. (New York: Image Books, 1962), 2:144-55.

[4] St. Thomas Aquinas, *Summa Theologica* Q. 10, Art. 2.

[5] Swinburne, *Coherence*, p. 1.

[6] Wolterstorff, "Everlasting," p. 93. See also Norman Kretzman, "Omniscience and Immutability," in *Readings in Philosophy of Religion*, ed. Baruch A. Brody (Englewood Cliffs, NJ: Prentice-Hall, 1974), pp. 366-76.

The cosmological argument based upon it goes roughly as follows: The universe must be of a finite age since to claim that it is of infinite age would postulate the existence of an actual infinity of moments.[7] But we know that an actual infinity is logically impossible. Hence, the universe must be of finite age. However, if the universe is finite, then it must have been created. Since nothing can begin to exist without a cause, the universe must have been caused to exist. Whatever caused the universe to exist must itself be uncaused. This being is God.

It is a short step from this argument to the concept of an eternal God. If the universe can be shown to be of finite age because of the impossibility of an actual infinite, then by similar reasoning we must affirm an eternal God. If God were in time, or subject to change, the question would arise whether or not God had a beginning. Since an actual infinite cannot exist, God must have had a beginning also. But this is impossible. Therefore, God must not be the kind of being which can experience change and, hence, is outside of time.[8]

The radicalness of this conclusion has not been appreciated, and most of the contemporary debate ignores arguments such as Hackett's, which rely on the *kalam* principle. Keith Ward, for example, has argued that we should conceive of God as having both a necessary, unchanging aspect and a contingent, changing aspect.[9] Both these aspects, or polarities, are part of the being of God and, as such, are uncreated and everlasting. However, such a conception is logically impossible in Hackett's view. God cannot have a contingent, changing aspect. If He did, either an actual infinite would exist or the question, as noted above, must be asked, how did God come into being?

---

[7]One might respond that there can be no infinite number of moments since past moments no longer exist. However, this fact about the past would make no difference since it would be possible that each past moment would leave a permanent record which would exist on into the future. Hence, even though the past moments no longer exist, the permanent record of their existence would. Hence, if there were an infinite number of past moments, there would be an infinite number of permanent records.

[8]Hackett, *Resurrection of Theism*, pp. 196-97.

[9]Ward, *Rational Theology*, pp. 164-65.

II

One recent attempt has been made to reconcile the eternality of God required by the *kalam* principle and the personality of God apparently demanded by revelation. William Lane Craig has argued that God was outside of time before creation and inside time after creation.[10] God must exist within time after creation in so far as He sustains a true relation to His temporal creation. But this, Craig claims, does not mean that God changes. He states: "This understanding does not involve any change in God; rather He is simply related to changing things."[11] The picture seems to be that after creation God is within time without being affected by time.

This response simply sidesteps the issues which the personalists raise, namely, how is God related to the changing world? Many world religions accept a transcendental reality which relates to the changing world. Taoism, for example, affirms the existence of an unchanging reality, the Tao, with which the world of experience is in some way identical. This kind of relationship to the world represents nothing close to a theistic conception. What the theist needs is a relationship of activity, knowledge, willing, loving, forgiving, and redeeming. Craig's suggestion leaves the nature of the relationship unexplained, which is precisely why the personalists bring the issue against the classical concept in the first place.

The problem of God's relationship to time concerns the essential characteristics of God. Craig's proposal rests on a confusion. The personalists make a stronger claim than simply that God is in time. They contend that time is part of the being of God, since God changes in response to His creation. Thus, what the personalist means by the temporality of God is very different from Craig's notion, raising the question of what he means by saying that God is in time if God undergoes no change.

Craig seems to suggest that the temporal properties of God, either as being eternal or as being everlasting, are accidental properties of God. Thus, God can accidentally be eternal before creation and accidentally everlasting afterwards.

This, it seems to me, has two problems. First, if God is absolutely necessary, as the classical tradition describes God, then the claim is that God is essentially timeless, that

---

[10]William Lane Craig, "God, Time, and Eternity," *Religious Studies* 14 (1978):502.

[11]Ibid.

is to say, timelessness is part of the essence of God. Hence, God cannot simply take up temporality without thereby ceasing to be God. Secondly, if timelessness is an accidental property of God, then the question of why God is that way rather than another way seems an obvious one to ask. What caused God to be in time rather than outside time? On Craig's conception it is doubtful that God's absoluteness can be preserved. For these reasons, the middle ground cannot be maintained.

Therefore, it seems reasonable to conclude that the options are mutually exclusive: either God is eternal and outside time or God is everlasting and time is part of God's being.

III

The crux, then, will be whether the *kalam* principle is true or not. If it is, then the personalist's position is unacceptable. This would, so to speak, cut the Gordian knot for the contemporary debate. If one of the two alternatives is logically impossible, then there is obviously no problem.

Everything seems to ride on the impossibility or the possibility of the actual infinite. Is the *kalam* principle true or is it not? Unfortunately, I very seriously doubt that this issue can be resolved. We can see why if we examine an interesting parallel between the argument for the impossibility of the actual infinite and the ontological argument for the existence of God.

One of the consequences of the work of Alvin Plantinga has been the demonstration of the inadequacy of the test of conceivability for determining logical possibility or impossibility.[12] He shows this by analyzing the concept of maximal greatness. A maximally excellent being in any particular possible world is one that has the properties of omniscience, omnipresence, omnipotence, and omnibenevolence. A maximally great being is a being that is maximally excellent in all possible worlds. If God is a maximally great being, then He must exist, since by definition a maximally great being exists in all possible worlds, including this one.

---

[12] I do not claim that this is how Plantinga sees his own work. However, it seems to me that it follows from his conclusion in, for example, *The Nature of Necessity* (New York: Oxford University Press, 1974), pp. 217-21.

The problem with this proof, as Plantinga recognizes, lies in proving the possibility of maximal greatness. It seems that one can conceive both of a world with a maximally great being and of a world without one. But since these are mutually impossible possibilities, something must be wrong. The problem, I believe, lies with the test. Simple conceivability or having the capacity to describe a state of affairs without obvious logical contradiction are not sufficient techniques for proving the logical possibility of a particular state of affairs. We can conceive of worlds which, if possible, will exclude the possibility of other worlds we can conceive. Hence, the test by itself cannot answer our question about the possibility of a maximally great being.

A similar situation exists with respect to the *kalam* principle. It is a very subtle and elusive idea: that an actual infinite is impossible. But conceivability or non-conceivability will not show us whether it is possible or impossible, since sometimes it seems conceivable and at other times it does not.

The problematic nature of the principle is highlighted by the way the proponents of the principle make their case. The mode of argument is not to derive the conclusion from more fundamental propositions. Rather, the argument relies on an intuition of the impossibility revealed in the perusal of a number of different thought experiments.

Craig, for example, proposes that we consider a library with an infinite number of books.[13] The supposition that an actual infinite number is possible, he suggests, leads to a number of problems for the librarian. If the library contains an infinite number of books, each of which is numbered by a natural number, what number could the librarian assign to a new addition? Craig concludes that adding any new book would be impossible since there would be no number to give it. But this is absurd, he argues, since it is always possible to number an actually existing thing such as a book. From this it follows that an actual infinite is impossible.

Craig relies on the capacity of the mind to intuit the impossibility here. Hence, we must conclude, as Hackett states, that "The notion of such an actually infinite series is simply not logically intelligible to any person who fully and clearly understands what such a notion involves."[14]

The point I raise here is about the way the impossibility of the actual infinite is proved. Its proof, or disproof, lies in its intuitive plausibility or implausibility. However,

---

[13]Craig, Kalam *Argument*, pp. 82-84.

[14]Hackett, *Reconstruction*, p. 101.

as the work of Plantinga indicates, this is a quite problematic way of proving logical possibility. This difficulty raises significant doubt that this way of proving things will do the job.

The difficulty is compounded by a confusion about the concept of infinity which Richard Sorabji identifies. Craig's thought experiments rely on the intuitive implausibility of adding to an infinite number of things. Hence, it seems very odd to add a book to a library already containing an infinite number of books. Sorabji suggests that any infinite set will not contain everything.[15] Thus, it seems to make perfect sense to add to an infinite set some of those things it does not contain. The problem with the actual infinite is in seeing how we can add to it. What Craig's librarian needs to do is to shift each book one space to the right, thus freeing a space for the new addition. The librarian would not be adding a new space, only rearranging the spaces already available. And since there is an infinite amount of shelf space, there will always be room to shift the old books to make room for the new.

The idea that an infinite set does not contain everything is illustrated by a mathematical example. The infinite set of natural numbers does not contain all numbers. Here I use the mathematical example to show that we use the idea regularly. It is not an intuitively absurd notion.

Given this idea about the actual infinite, Craig's library loses some of its apparent paradox. His example only illustrates the logic of the actual infinite, but not anything which shows that the actual infinite is impossible (one man's *modus ponens* is another man's *modus tolens*, so to speak). As Sorabji explains,

> Once it is seen like this, the outcome should no longer seem an absurdity which can discredit the idea of an actual infinite. It should instead be seen as an explicable truth about infinity. It may be a surprising truth, even an exhilarating and delightful truth, but a truth for which we can perfectly well see the reasons, when we reflect on the idea sticking out beyond the far end.[16]

---

[15]Richard Sorabji, *Time, Creation and the Continuum* (Ithaca, NY: Cornell University Press, 1983), p. 222.

[16]Ibid., p. 223.

IV

If the possibility of an actual infinite is undecidable by the standard test for logical possibility or impossibility, where does that leave us? There is another kind of argument for logical possibility, which I call a possibility proof. The idea behind a possibility proof is that if we can show something to exist, then *ipso facto* we have shown it to be logically possible. In other words, what is actual is possible.[17]

Maybe there is a possibility proof which will answer our question, one that will enable us to decide between the possibility or the impossibility of an actual infinite. If we begin the discussion this way, we find evidence that the *kalam* principle is false. If an actual infinite is not ruled out from the beginning, the personalist's argument for God's existence indicates that there is in fact an actual infinite. Hence, we could conclude that an actual infinite is possible, since it is actual.

Personalism defines the parameters of the concept of God using the concept of personal causation. P. F. Strawson has argued persuasively that our modern conceptual scheme recognizes two kinds of agency, bodies and persons.[18] The theist, while admitting that a worldview based on impersonal causation can be constructed, argues that the best worldview takes personal causation as its foundation. This leads to a concept of God as a person, one who knows, acts, feels, and forgives, similar to the way human persons know, act, feel, and forgive, only on a much larger scale. Furthermore, it is claimed, this means that God in His being changes in His loving and redeeming responses to His creation. Therefore, if God is essentially a person who changes and is uncreated, an actual infinite of moments must have passed.

The import of this model lies in two considerations. First, if the argument is successful and thereby shows that God exists, the *Kalam* argument is shown to be irrelevant. One need not appeal to the *Kalam* argument to prove God's existence if

---

[17]Swinburne suggests this as a test for the coherence of the concept of God. See *Coherence*, pp. 294-97. Leibniz also sought such a proof as a condition for the cogency of the ontological argument. Cf. G.W. Leibniz, "Critical Remarks Concerning the General Part of Descartes' Principles," in *Monadology and Other Philosophical Essays*, trans. Paul Schrecker and Anne Martin Schrecker (Indianapolis: Bobbs-Merrill, 1965), pp. 27-29.

[18]P.F. Strawson, *Individuals* (New York: Anchor Books, 1963), p. 113.

God's existence has already been proved. Secondly, the personalist model shows that an actual infinite is both possible and actual.

V

There is another reason why it seems difficult for the theist to accept the *kalam* principle. It can be said, in a frivolous way, that an actual infinite must exist since God exists and God is an infinite being. Craig has responded, rightly in my mind, that this mistakes the kind of infinity one is affirming. The *kalam* principle can accept the description of God as an infinite being when "infinite" is used as a qualifying term intended to indicate what God is not, rather than what God is. The objectionable kind of infinity is a numerical concept which expresses a number or volume, an infinite number of things or an infinite volume of stuff; as Craig describes it, "an actually infinite collection of definite and distinct finite members."[19] This latter kind of infinity is objectionable in a way that the former is not.

However, while this rebuttal by Craig is appropriate for some objections, the response seems inadequate for a different kind of infinity which the existence of God entails. I can show this if I am allowed a couple of assumptions which seem *prima facie* plausible. First, God knows particulars. That is to say, God knows, for example, not only the essence of humanity, but God also knows each and every individual human being in his or her particularity. Secondly, God Himself is an object of knowledge, if not for humans, at least for Himself. Thirdly, God is omniscient, where "omniscient" is defined as "knowing all that is logically possible to know."

Given these three assumptions, it seems that an actual infinite is entailed by God's existence. Since God is omniscient and knows particulars, then God must know every particular thing. There is an infinite number of particular things to know. Therefore, there must be an actual infinite.

The heart of this argument will lie in whether one can prove that there is an infinite number of things to know. There will be, I admit, a sense in which this premise begs the issue. If the *kalam* principle states that the actual infinite is impossible, then surely it is unfair to state that there is an infinite number of things to know. *Ex hypothesi* that state of affairs is impossible.

---

[19]Craig, Kalam *Argument*, p. 70.

The reason that I state the premise this way is to lead into a discussion of the mathematical concept of a potential infinite. The *kalam* argument admits that, in a sense, there is an infinite number of points on a line. However, this kind of infinite is a potential infinite, not an actual infinite. Hackett describes this kind of infinity as "indefinite extension." The set of natural numbers, for example, does not constitute an actual infinite number of things; rather it is a set of things which can always be extended; one where there will always be a larger number from the one picked out; or one where there is no largest number. He claims that this kind of infinity is very different from the kind of infinity which, he claims, is impossible.[20]

Craig makes a similar claim with respect to numbers and points on a line. The infinity of points on a line is not an actual infinite, but a potential infinite. One could interpret this as meaning something like this: for every two points one finds on a line, there will always be a point between them. But, according to Craig, these points do not exist until they are constructed.[21]

This response seems adequate as a way to deny one kind of actual infinite, yet it seems inadequate as a response to the problem of God's knowledge of numbers or of points on a line. If God is omniscient, there is no such thing as a potential infinity of numbers or points.[22] God knows each number and point in its particularity. What holds from the human standpoint, that we cannot count to infinity, cannot hold with respect to God. God must have counted to infinity whether or not we can; therefore, God must know an infinite number of things. Otherwise, God will not be omniscient, since there would be something He does not know, namely, particular numbers or particular points on a line.

A concomitant problem arises with respect to God's knowledge of Himself. On the Thomistic model, God is perfectly simple, without difference within His being. According to this concept, God's self-knowledge is not properly said to be knowledge

---

[20]Hackett, *Reconstruction*, p. 100.

[21]Craig, Kalam *Argument*, pp. 65-66. Craig finds intuitionist mathematics congenial because of its denial of mathematical realism. If numbers are not real, then obvious counter-examples such as the set of natural numbers are eliminated. Cf. Kalam *Argument*, pp. 93ff.

[22]I think the idea of a potential infinity of, for example, points on a line should be distinguished from the idea of logical possibility. The points on a line make up an actually existing object in a way that a logically possible world does not.

of an infinite number of things. Nor, for that matter, is His knowledge of particular finite things properly said to be knowledge of an infinite number of things. But many reject this concept of God's simplicity.

Hackett, for example, states:

> If anything, God is . . . the most complex of all beings, since the notion of divine simplicity would imply that no conceptually determinate properties were genuinely attributable to the Divine Essence, with the result that God would be totally unknowable through conceptual reason or discursive intellect. It might even be argued that the divine-simplicity view would logically entail the non-existence of God, since it seems plausible to maintain that whatever is real or exists must have certain determinate properties which distinguish it from other entities.[23]

God is, on Hackett's view, the "most complex of beings." But this raises the issue for Hackett, in a way that the Thomist does not face, of God's self-knowledge. It seems plausible to say that there is an infinite number of things to know about God. From the human perspective, complete knowledge of God is impossible. Thus, we shall forever be learning more and more about God. We might say that, from the human standpoint, God's being presents us with a potential infinite. For everything we know about God, there is always something else to learn. But can we say the same thing about God's self-knowledge? It seems to me that we cannot. God, because He is omniscient, must know everything there is to know about Himself. Hence, if God is an infinitely complex being, then there is an actual infinite of the kind the *kalam* principle finds objectionable.

My argument here is one which finds a certain sympathy with Leibniz. Leibniz argued that the concept of extension is incoherent. His argument assumed that the mental operation of dividing a so-called extended object sufficed to show that the results of the division were real. Hence, the fact that we could conceive of dividing a piece of wood sufficed to show that the parts of the piece of wood existed.[24]

---

[23]Hackett, *Reconstruction*, pp. 89-90.

[24]Leibniz, "Monadology," in *Monadology and Other Philosophical Essays*, p. 159, par. 65. See also Nicholas Rescher, *Leibniz: An Introduction to his Philosophy* (Oxford: Blackwell's, 1979), pp. 99-102.

In the same way, I want to claim that the points on a line are real, if not for us, certainly for God. They must exist and be objects of knowledge for Him. Hence, there are certain kinds of actual infinities of the kind which the *kalam* argument assumes to be impossible.

The proponents of the *kalam* principle may respond with the claim that God's knowledge of the world is different from ours. Since God has the power to have all facts before Him, He can, so to speak, intuitively grasp the whole. As we perceive a circle in its entirety and not in little bits, so God perceives the world.[25]

This argument, it seems to me, is only acceptable if one believes that God does not know particulars. Thus, God would have a certain kind of grasp of the universe in its wholeness, but would not know any of its parts. This conception may be acceptable to some, but it should be objectionable to any classical theist. If God knows the universe in its particularity, He knows the book that I have in my hand, He knows the parts of the book that I have in my hand, He knows the parts of the parts of the book that I have in my hand, and so on to infinity.

Where does this leave us? Initially we had two options with respect to the concept of God: Thomism and personalism. The *kalam* principle is best seen as an independent argument for the classical concept of God, at least with respect to God's eternality. However, the support the *kalam* principle gives is ephemeral. One must rely on an intuition which sometimes seems reliable, but at other times seems not. In addition, a question remains of the compatibility of the *kalam* argument with theism.

The conclusion seems to be that we must look to either Thomism or personalism for our understanding of God. We may conclude either that God is in time or that God is outside time, but in neither case should the argument rest on the possibility or the impossibility of an actual infinite.

---

[25]Cf. Craig, Kalam *Argument*, pp. 151-52, and Hackett, *Resurrection*, pp. 286-87. William P. Alston has recently argued that God's knowledge should best be considered as intuitive rather than discursive. I believe that we can accept this conclusion, which is the conclusion Hackett and Craig accept, but also claim that God knows particulars in the way necessary for the argument in this paper. For God's mode of knowledge, that is, how God knows particulars, intuitively or discursively, does not affect the object of knowledge. Cf. William P. Alston, "Does God Have Beliefs?" *Religious Studies* 22 (1986):287-306.

The Teleological Argument And The Anthropic Principle

William Lane Craig

Westmont College and

Université Catholique de Louvain

INTRODUCTION

Widely thought to have been demolished by Hume and Darwin, the teleological argument for God's existence has nonetheless continued during this century to find able defenders in F.R. Tennant, Peter Bertocci, and Stuart C. Hackett. All of these have appealed to what Tennant called "wider teleology," which emphasizes the necessary conditions for the existence and evolution of intelligent life, rather than specific instances of purposive design. Unfortunately, they could speak of this wider teleology for the most part only in generalities, for example, "the fitness of the inorganic to minister to life," but could furnish few specific examples of experimental fact to illustrate this cosmic teleology.

In recent years, however, the scientific community has been stunned by its discovery of how complex and sensitive a nexus of conditions must be given in order for the universe to permit the origin and evolution of intelligent life on Earth. The universe appears, in fact, to have been incredibly fine-tuned from the moment of its inception for the production of intelligent life on Earth at this point in cosmic history. In the various fields of physics and astrophysics, classical cosmology, quantum mechanics, and biochemistry, various discoveries have repeatedly disclosed that the existence of intelligent carbon-based life on Earth at this time depends upon a delicate balance of physical and cosmological quantities, such that were any one of these quantities to be slightly altered, the balance would be destroyed and life would not exist.

Let us briefly review some of the cosmological and physical quantities that have been found to exhibit this delicate balance necessary for the existence of intelligent life on Earth at this epoch in cosmic history.[1]

EXAMPLES OF WIDER TELEOLOGY

Physics and Astrophysics

To begin with the most general of conditions, it was shown by G. J. Whitrow in 1955 that intelligent life would be impossible except in a universe of three basic dimensions. When formulated in three dimensions, mathematical physics possesses many unique properties which are necessary prerequisites for the existence of rational information-processing observers like ourselves. Moreover, dimensionality plays a key role in determining the form of the laws of physics and in fashioning the roles played by the constants of nature. For example, it is due to its basic three-dimensionality that the world possesses the chemistry that it does, which furnishes some key conditions necessary for the existence of life. Whitrow could not answer the question why the actual universe happens to possess three dimensions, but noted that if it did not, then we should not be here to ask the question.

More specifically, the values of the various forces of nature appear to be fine-tuned for the existence of intelligent life. The world is conditioned principally by the values

---

[1] I depend for the following section on the impressive compilations by John D. Barrow and Frank J. Tipler, *The Anthropic Cosmological Principle* (Oxford: Clarendon Press, 1986) and John Leslie, "The Prerequisites of Life in Our Universe," in *Newton and the New Direction in Science*, ed. G.V. Coyne, M. Heller, J. Zycinski (Vatican: Citta del Vaticano, 1988). Detailed discussion and documentation may be found there.

of the fundamental constants α (the fine structure constant, or electromagnetic interaction), m_n/m_e (proton to electron mass ratio, α_G (gravitation), α_w (the weak force), and α_s (the strong force). When one mentally assigns different values to these constants or forces, one discovers that in fact the number of observable universes, that is to say, universes capable of supporting intelligent life, is very small. Just a slight variation in any one of these values would render life impossible.

For example, if α_s were increased as much as 1%, nuclear resonance levels would be so altered that almost all carbon would be burned into oxygen; an increase of 2% would preclude formation of protons out of quarks, preventing the existence of atoms. Furthermore, weakening α_s by as much as 5% would unbind deuteron, which is essential to stellar nucleosynthesis, leading to a universe composed only of hydrogen. It has been estimated that α_s must be within 0.8 and 1.2 of its actual strength or all elements of atomic weight greater than four would not have formed. Or again, if α_w had been appreciably stronger, then the Big Bang's nuclear burning would have proceeded past helium to iron, making fusion-powered stars impossible. But if it had been much weaker, then we should have had a universe entirely of helium. Or again, if α_G had been a little greater, all stars would have been red dwarfs, which are too cold to support life-bearing planets. If it had been a little smaller, the universe would have been composed exclusively of blue giants which burn too briefly for life to develop. According to Davies, changes in either α_G or electromagnetism by only one part in 10^{40} would have spelled disaster for stars like the sun. Moreover, the fact that life can develop on a planet orbiting a star at the right distance depends on the close proximity of the spectral temperature of starlight to the molecular binding energy. Were it greatly to exceed this value, living organisms would be sterilized or destroyed; but were it far below this value, then the photochemical reactions necessary to life would proceed too slowly for life to exist. Or again, atmospheric composition, upon which life depends, is constrained by planetary mass. But planetary mass is the inevitable consequence of electromagnetic and gravitational interactions. And there simply is no physical theory which can explain the numerical values of α and m_n/m_e that determine electromagnetic interaction.

Moreover, life depends upon the operation of certain principles in the quantum realm. For example, the Pauli Exclusion Principle, which states that no more than one particle of a particular kind and spin is permitted in a single quantum state, plays a key role in nature. It guarantees the stability of matter and the size of atomic and molecular structures and creates the shell structure of atomic electrons. In a world not governed by this principle, only compact, superdense bodies could exist, providing little scope for complex structures or living organisms. Or again, quantization is also essential for the existence and stability of atomic systems. In quantum physics, the atom is not conceived on the model of a tiny solar system with each electron in its orbit around the nucleus. Such a model would be unstable because any orbit could be an arbitrary distance from the nucleus. But in quantum physics, there is only one orbital radius available to an electron, so that, for example, all hydrogen atoms are alike. As a consequence, atomic systems and matter are stable and therefore life-permitting.

Classical Cosmology

Several of the constants mentioned in the foregoing section also play a crucial role in determining the temporal phases of the development of the universe and thus control features of the universe essential to life. For example, α_G and m_n/m_e constrain (i) the main sequence stellar lifetime, (ii) the time before which the expansion dynamics of the expanding universe are determined by radiation rather than matter, (iii) the time after which the universe is cool enough for atoms and molecules to form, (iv) the time necessary for protons to decay, and (v) the Planck time.

Furthermore, a fine balance must exist between the gravitational and weak interactions. If the balance were upset in one direction, the universe would have been constituted by 100% helium in its early phase, which would have made it impossible for life to exist now. If the balance were tipped in the other direction, then it would not have been possible for neutrinos to blast the envelopes of supernovae into space and so distribute the heavy elements essential to life.

Furthermore, the difference between the masses of the neutron and the proton is also part of a very delicate coincidence which is crucial to a life-supporting environment. This difference prevents protons from decaying into neutrons, which, if it happened, would make life impossible. This ratio is also balanced with the electron mass, for if the neutron mass failed to exceed the proton mass by a little more than the electron mass, then atoms would simply collapse.

Considerations of classical cosmology allow us to introduce a new parameter, S, the entropy per baryon in the universe, which is about 10^9. Unless S were $< 10^{11}$, galaxies would not have been able to form, making planetary life impossible. S is itself a consequence of the baryon asymmetry in the universe, which arises from the inexplicably built-in asymmetry of quarks ever anti-quarks prior to 10^{-6} seconds after the Big Bang.

In investigating the initial conditions of the Big Bang, one is also confronted with two arbitrary parameters governing the expansion of the universe: Ω_0, related to the density of the universe, and H_0, related to the speed of the expansion. Observations indicate that at 10^{-43} seconds after the Big Bang the universe was expanding at a fantastically special rate of speed with a total density close to the critical value on the borderline between recollapse and everlasting expansion. Hawking estimated that even a decrease of one part in a million million when the temperature of the universe was 10^{10} degrees would have resulted in the universe's recollapse long ago; a similar increase would have precluded the galaxies from condensing out of the expanding matter. At the Planck time, 10^{-43} seconds after the Big Bang, the density of the universe must have apparently been within about one part in 10^{60} of the critical density at which space is flat. This results in the so-called "flatness problem": why is the universe expanding at just such a rate that space is Euclidean rather than curved? A second problem that arises is the "homogeneity problem." There is a very narrow range of initial conditions which must obtain if galaxies are to form later. If the initial inhomogeneity ratio were $> 10^{-2}$, then non-uniformities would condense prematurely into black holes before the stars form. But if the ratio were $< 10^{-5}$, inhomogeneities would be insufficient to condense into galaxies. Because matter in the universe is clumped into galaxies, which is a necessary condition of life, the initial inhomogeneity ratio appears to be incredibly fine-tuned. Thirdly, there is the "isotropy problem." The temperature of the universe is amazing in its isotropy: it varies by only one part in a thousand over the whole of the sky. But at very early stages of the universe, the different regions of the universe were causally disjointed, since light beams could not travel fast enough to connect the rapidly receding regions. How then did these unconnected regions all happen to possess the same temperature and radiation density? Penrose has calculated that in the absence of new physical principles to explain this, "the accuracy of the Creator's aim" when he selected this world from the set of physically possible ones would need to have been at least of the order of one part in $10^{10(123)}$.

Contemporary cosmologists have found an answer to these three problems—or at least seem certain that they are on its track—in inflationary models of the early universe. According to this adjustment to the standard Big Bang cosmology, between 10^{-43} and 10^{-35} seconds after the Big Bang, the universe underwent an exponentially rapid inflation of space faster than the speed of light. This inflationary epoch resulted in the nearly flat curvature of space, pushed inhomogeneities beyond our horizon, and served to bury us far within a single region of space-time whose parts were causally connected at pre-inflationary times.

Inflationary scenarios have problems of their own—such as getting inflation started, getting it to end without excess turbulence, and having it produce irregularities just right for galaxy formation. Indeed, it is interesting to note that Hawking has recently declared both the so-called "old inflationary model" and the "new inflationary model" to be "now dead as a scientific theory"—though he still holds out hope for Linde's more recent "chaotic inflationary model."[2] Whether this model proves to be any more successful than its predecessors remains to be seen; the whole inflationary scenario seems rather *ad hoc*, and one cannot help but suspect that much of the attraction to such models is due to the desire to escape the sort of inferences as Penrose's conclusion above. More importantly, however, inflationary scenarios seem to require the same sort of fine-tuning which some theorists thought these models had eliminated. For example, in order to proceed appropriately, inflation requires that the two theoretical components of Einstein's cosmological constant, "bare lambda" and "quantum lambda," cancel each other out with an enormously precise though inexplicable accuracy. A change in the strengths of either α_G or α_w by as little as one part in 10^{100} would destroy this cancellation on which our lives depend. So although inflationary models may succeed in providing a unifying explanation of some of the forces which play a role in classical cosmology, it does not thereby dispense with the appearance of fine-tuning or teleology.

---

[2] Stephen Hawking, *A Brief History of Time: from the Big Bang to Black Holes* (New York: Bantam Books, 1988), p.132.

Biochemistry

Life which is descended from a simpler form of life and which ultimately came into existence spontaneously must be based on water, carbon dioxide, and the basic compounds of the elements C, H, O, and N. Each of these possesses unique properties which, while not sufficient for the existence of life, are necessary conditions of it.

Water, for example, is one of the strongest substances known to science. Its specific heat, surface tension, and most of its other physical properties have anomalous values higher or lower than any other known material. The fact that its solid phase is less dense than its liquid phase, so that ice floats, is virtually a unique property in nature. Its melting point, boiling point, and vaporization point are all anomalously higher than those of other substances. For example, when calculated by atomic weight and number, the boiling point of water would be expected to be -100°C rather than $+100^\circ$C. The disparity is due to its strong hydrogen bonds, which are difficult to break. Furthermore, because the H-O-H angle in water is so close to the ideal tetrahedral structure, water can form such a structure with very little strain on the bonds. As a result, it tends to polymerize into an open structure, so that ice is less dense than water. This property of water is essential to life, for were ice more dense than water, it would sink to the bottom of bodies of water, where it would remain in the deepest parts until eventually all lakes and oceans would be solidly frozen. Instead, ice forms a protective skin on the surface of reservoirs of water. Water also has a higher specific heat than almost any organic compound. This property allows water to be a store of heat and so stabilize the environment. The thermal conductivity of water is also higher than that of most liquids, which again permits water to act as a temperature stabilizer on the environment. Water has, moreover, a higher heat of vaporization than any known substance. This makes water the best possible coolant by evaporation, and living creatures make extensive use of it in temperature control. Water's high surface tension, exceeded by very few substances, serves to make biochemical reactions more rapid; and the way water bonds shapes organic molecules such as enzymes and nucleic acids into their biologically active forms and permits the formation of cell walls and membranes.

The elements H, O, and C are the most abundant elements in living organisms. They possess many unique properties and are vital to chemical reactions necessary to sustain life. For example, CO_2 has the property, unique among gases, of having at ordinary temperatures about the same concentration of molecules per unit volume in water as in air. This enables CO_2 to undergo perpetual exchange between living organisms and their environment, so that it is everywhere available for photosynthesis and thereby for molecular synthesis. The element N, on the other hand, is a rare element on Earth, but it does make up 80% of the earth's atmosphere, which is a unique stroke of fortune for earth's living organisms.

This selective sampling of physical and cosmological quantities which are necessary conditions of the existence of intelligent life on Earth at this point in cosmic history illustrates the sort of wider teleology which Tennant emphasized, but could only dimly envision. The discoveries of contemporary science in this regard are particularly impressive for two reasons: (1) The delicate balance of conditions upon which life depends is characterized by the interweaving of conditions, such that life depends for its existence, not merely upon each individual condition's possessing a value within very narrow limits, but also upon ratios or interactions between values and forces which must likewise lie within narrow parameters. The situation is thus not comparable to a roulette wheel in Monte Carlo's yielding a certain winning number (which would be susceptible to the old objection that any number is equally improbable); nor even yet to all the roulette wheels (each representing a physical quantity or constant) in Monte Carlo's turning up simultaneously certain numbers within narrowly circumscribed limits (say, wheel 1 must show 72 or 73 while wheel 2 must show 27-29, etc.); rather it is like all the roulette wheels in Monte Carlo's yielding simultaneously numbers within narrowly prescribed limits and those numbers bearing certain precise relations among themselves (say, the number of wheel 3 must be one-half the square of the number of wheel 17 and twice the number of wheel 6). It seems clear that worlds not permitting intelligent life are more to be expected than life-permitting worlds. (2) The constants and quantities which go to make up this complex nexus of conditions are apparently independent of one another. The development of inflationary models ought to cause us to be cautious in making such a claim; nevertheless, it is the case that there seems to be no nomological necessity requiring the quantities and constants of nature to be related as they are. The value of S, for example, seems to be utterly unrelated to Ω_0, H_0, or inflationary scenarios. But even if it were possible to reduce all the physical and cosmological quantities to a single equation governing the whole of nature, such a complex equation could itself be seen as the supreme instance of teleology and design. Hence, some of those whose hopes seem to lie in the discovery of such an equation are forced to assert that such an equation must be necessarily true; that is to say, there is really only one logically possible set of physical constants and forces. But such a hypothesis seems clearly outlandish. As Nagel observes, none of the statements of natural laws in the various sciences are logically necessary, since their denials are not formally contradictory; moreover, the appropriate procedure in science should then cease to be experimentation, but be deductive proofs in the manner of mathematics.[3] Hence, the notion that the nomological necessity of such an equation should reduce to logical necessity seems obviously false.

THE ANTHROPIC PRINCIPLE

This pattern of discoveries has compelled many scientists to conclude that such a delicate balance cannot be simply dismissed as coincidence, but requires some sort of account. Traditionally, such considerations would have been taken as evidence of divine design—one thinks of Paley's teleological argument in his *Natural Theology*, for example. Loath to admit the God-hypothesis, however, many scientists are seeking an alternative in the Anthropic Principle, and a tremendous debate involving both scientists and philosophers has broken out concerning this principle, a debate which has spilled over into the popular press and captured the attention of science-minded laymen. The attempt to come to grips with the appearance of cosmic teleology has forced many scientists beyond physics into metaphysics, so that the boundaries between science and philosophy have become ineradicably blurred, well-illustrating George Gale's remark that "we are now entering a phase of scientific activity during which the physicist has out-run his philosophical base-camp, and, finding himself cut off from conceptual supplies, he is ready and waiting for some relief from his philosophical comrades-in-arms."[4] The theistic philosopher can therefore without apology or embarrassment introduce his metaphysical commitment to theism as an at

---

[3]Ernst Nagel, *The Structure of Science*, 2d ed. (Indianapolis: Hackett, 1979), pp. 53-54.

[4]George Gale, "Some Metaphysical Perplexities in Contemporary Physics" (Paper presented at the 1985 meeting of the Society of Metaphysics).

least equally plausible, if not superior, alternative explanation to metaphysical, naturalistic accounts of the complex order of the universe.

Exposition

First proposed by Brandon Carter in 1974,[5] the Anthropic Principle has assumed a number of different forms, generating a great deal of confusion concerning what it is precisely that the principle means to assert. In their recent monumental book, *The Anthropic Cosmological Principle*, physicists John Barrow and Frank Tipler state various versions of the principle, the most fundamental being the Weak Anthropic Principle (WAP):

> WAP: The observed values of all physical and cosmological quantities are not equally probable, but they take on values restricted by the requirement that there exist sites where carbon-based life can evolve and by the requirement that the Universe be old enough for it to have already done so.[6]

Barrow and Tipler regard WAP as "in no way speculative or controversial,"[7] since it is "just a restatement . . . of one of the most important and well-established principles of science: that it is essential to take into account the limitations of one's measuring apparatus when interpreting one's observations."[8] For example, if we were calculating the fraction of galaxies that lie within certain ranges of brightness, our observations would be biased toward the brighter ones, since we cannot see the dim ones so easily. Or again, a ratcatcher may say that all rats are bigger than six inches because that is the size of his traps. Similarly, any observed properties of the universe which may initially appear astonishingly improbable can only be seen in their true perspective after

---

[5]Brandon Carter, "Large Number Coincidences and the Anthropic Principle," in *Confrontation of Cosmological Theories with Observational Data*, ed. M.S. Longair (Boston: D. Reidel, 1974), pp. 291-98.

[6]Barrow and Tipler, *Anthropic Principle*, p. 15.

[7]Ibid., p. 16.

[8]Ibid., p. 23.

we have accounted for the fact that certain properties could not be observed by us, were they to obtain, because we can only observe those compatible with our own existence. "The basic features of the Universe, including such properties as its shape, size, age, and laws of change must be *observed* to be of a type that allows the evolution of the observers, for if intelligent life did not evolve in an otherwise possible universe, it is obvious that no one would be asking the reason for the observed shape, size, age, and so forth of the universe."[9] Thus, our own existence acts as a selection effect in assessing the various properties of the universe. For example, a life form which evolved on an earthlike planet "must necessarily see the universe to be at least several billion years old and . . . several billion light years across," for this is the time necessary for the production of the elements essential to life and so forth.[10]

Now, we might ask, why is the "observed" in the quotation in the above paragraph italicized? Why not omit the word altogether? The answer is that the resulting statement

1. The basic features of the universe must be of a type that allows the evolution of observers

is undoubtedly false; for it is not logically or nomologically necessary that the universe embrace intelligent life. Rather what seems to be necessarily true is

2. If the universe is observed by observers which have evolved within it, then its basic features must be of a type that allows the evolution of observers within it.

But (2) seems quite trivial; it does nothing to explain why the universe in fact has the basic features it does.

But Barrow and Tipler contend that while WAP appears to be true, but trivial, it has "far-reaching implications."[11] For the implication of WAP, which they seem to interpret along the lines of (2), is that no explanation of the basic features of the universe need be sought. This contention seems to be intimately connected with what is

---

[9]Ibid., pp. 1-2.

[10]Ibid., p. 3.

[11]Ibid., p. 2.

appropriate to be *surprised at*. The implication of WAP is that we ought not to be surprised at observing the universe to be as it is, for if it were not as it is, we could not observe it. For example, "No one should be surprised to find the universe to be as large as it is."[12] Or again, ". . . on Anthropic grounds, we should expect to observe a world possessing precisely three spatial dimensions."[13] Or again:

> We should emphasize once again that the enormous improbability of the evolution of intelligent life in general and *Homo sapiens* in particular does not mean we should be amazed we exist at all. This would make as much sense as Elizabeth II being amazed she is Queen of England. Even though the probability of a given Briton being monarch is about 10^{-8}, *someone* must be. Only if there is a monarch is it possible for the monarch to calculate the improbability of her particular existence. Similarly, only if an intelligent species does evolve is it possible for its members to ask how probable it is for an intelligent species to evolve. Both are examples of WAP self-selection in action.[110]

---

[110]F. B. Salisbury, *Nature* 224, 342 (1969), argued that the enormous improbability of a given gene, which we computed in the text, means that a gene is too unique to come into being by natural selection acting on chance mutations. WAP self-selection refutes this argument, as R. F. Doolittle in *Scientists confront creationism*, L. R. Godfrey (Norton, NY, 1983) has also pointed out.[14]

Here we have a far-reaching implication that goes considerably beyond the apparently trivial WAP. Accordingly, although Barrow and Tipler conflate WAP and the implications thought to follow from it, I want to distinguish these sharply and shall refer to these broader implications as the Anthropic Philosophy. It is this philosophical viewpoint, rather than WAP itself, that I believe, despite initial impressions, stands opposed to the teleological argument and constitutes scientific naturalism's most recent answer to that argument. According to the Anthropic Philosophy, an attitude of surprise

---

[12]Ibid., p. 18.
[13]Ibid., p. 247.
[14]Ibid., pp. 566, 575.

at the delicately balanced features of the universe essential to life is inappropriate; we should expect the universe to look this way. While this does not explain the origin of those features, it shows that no explanation is necessary. Hence, to posit a divine Designer is gratuitous.

Critique

WAP and Self-Selection

Now it needs to be emphasized that what the Anthropic Philosophy does *not* hold, despite the sloppy statements on this head often made by scientists, is that our existence as observers *explains* the basic features of the universe. The answer to the question "Why is the universe isotropic?" given by Collins and Hawking, ". . . the isotropy of the Universe is a consequence of our existence,"[15] is simply irresponsible and brings the Anthropic Philosophy into undeserved disrepute, for literally taken, such an answer would require some form of backward causation whereby the conditions of the early universe were brought about by us acting as efficient causes merely by our observing the heavens. But WAP neither asserts nor implies this; rather WAP holds that we must observe the universe to possess certain features (not that the universe must possess certain features) and the Anthropic Philosophy says that therefore these features ought not to surprise us or cry out for explanation. The self-selection effect affects our observations, not the basic features of the universe itself. If the Anthropic Philosophy held that the basic features of the universe were themselves brought about by our observations, then it could be rightly dismissed as fanciful. But the Anthropic Philosophy is much more subtle: it does not try to explain why the universe has the basic features it does, but contends that no explanation is needed, since we should not be surprised at observing what we do, our observations of those basic features being restricted by our own existence as observers.

But does the Anthropic Philosophy follow from the Anthropic Principle, as Barrow and Tipler claim? Let us concede that it follows from WAP that

---

[15]C.B. Collins and S.W. Hawking, "Why Is the Universe Isotropic?" *Astrophysical Journal* 180 (1973):317.

3. We should not be surprised that we do not observe features of the universe which are incompatible with our own existence.

For if the features of the universe were incompatible with our existence, we should not be here to notice it. Hence, it is not surprising that we do not observe such features. But it follows neither from WAP nor (3) that

4. We should not be surprised that we do observe features of the universe which are compatible with our existence.

For although the object of surprise in (4) might at first blush appear to be simply the contrapositive of the object of surprise in (3), this is mistaken. This can be clearly seen by means of an illustration (borrowed from John Leslie[16]): suppose you are dragged before a firing squad of 100 trained marksmen, all of them with rifles aimed at your heart, to be executed. The command is given; you hear the deafening sound of the guns. *And you observe that you are still alive*, that all of the 100 marksmen missed! Now while it is true that

5. You should not be surprised that you do not observe that you are dead,

nonetheless it is equally true that

6. You should be surprised that you do observe that you are alive.

Since the firing squad's missing you altogether is extremely improbable, the surprise expressed in (6) is wholly appropriate, though you are not surprised that you do not observe that you are dead, since if you were dead you could not observe it. Similarly, while we should not be surprised that we do not observe features of the universe which are incompatible with our existence, it is nevertheless true that

---

[16]John Leslie, "Anthropic Principle, World Ensemble, Design," *American Philosophical Quarterly* 19 (1982):150.

7. We should be surprised that we do observe features of the universe which are compatible with our existence,

in view of the enormous improbability that the universe should possess such features.

The reason the falsity of (7) does not follow from (3) is that subimplication fails for first order predicate calculus. For (3) may be schematized as

3′. ~S: (x) ([Fx• ~Cx]⊃ ~Ox)

where "S:" is an operator expressing "we should be surprised that" and "F" is "is a feature of the universe," "C" is "is compatible with our existence," and "O" is "is observed by us." And (7) may be schematized as

7′. S: (∃x) (Fx•Cx•Ox)

It is clear that the object of surprise in (7′) is not equivalent to the object of surprise in (3′); therefore the truth of (3′) does not entail the negation of (7′).[17]

Therefore, the attempt of the Anthropic Philosophy to stave off our surprise at the basic features of the universe fails. It does not after all follow from WAP that our surprise at the basic features of the universe is unwarranted or inappropriate and that they do not therefore cry out for explanation. But which features of the universe should thus surprise us? It is those which are necessary conditions of our existence and which seem extremely improbable or whose coincidence seems extremely improbable. Thus, we should amend (7) to read:

7*. We should be surprised that we do observe basic features of the universe which individually or collectively are excessively improbable and are necessary conditions of our own existence.

---

[17]Similarly, the falsity of (6) does not follow from the truth of (5), for (5) may be schematized as ~S: ~(∃x) ([Mx•~Ax]•Ox), where "M" is "is me," "O" is "is observed by me" and "A" is "is alive." From this it does not follow that ~S: (∃x) ([Mx•Ax]•Ox), which is the negation of (6).

Against (7*), the WAP is impotent.[18]

WAP and a World Ensemble

Now proponents of the Anthropic Philosophy will no doubt contend that I have missed the whole point of the WAP. For (7*) is true only if the basic features of our observable universe are co-extensive with the basic features of the Universe as a whole. But proponents of the Anthropic Philosophy avoid (7*) by conjoining to WAP the hypothesis of a World Ensemble, that is to say, the hypothesis that our observable universe is but one member of a collection of diverse universes that go to make up a wider Universe-as-a-Whole. Given the existence of this wider Universe, it is argued that all possible universes are actualized and that the WAP reveals why surprise at our being in a universe with basic features essential to life is inappropriate.

Various theories, some of them quite fantastic, have been offered for generating a World Ensemble. For example, Wheeler proposes a model of the oscillating universe in which each cycle emerges with a new set of physical laws and constants.[19] Linde suggests an inflationary model according to which our observable universe is but one

---

[18]Once the central fallacy is thus removed, Barrow and Tipler's argument in the lengthy quotation in the text seems to amount to little more than the old objection that any state of affairs is highly improbable and therefore the obtaining of the actual state of affairs requires no special explanation. But this objection is surely misconceived. What unprejudiced and right-minded person could possibly regard a chimpanzee's haphazardly typing out the complete plays and sonnets of Shakespeare as equally probable with any chaotic series of letters? The objection fails to reckon with the difference between randomness, order, and complexity. On the first level of randomness, there is a non-denumerably infinite number of chaotic sequences, e.g., "adfzwj," each of which is equally improbable and which collectively could serve to exhaust all sequences typed by the ape. But the meta-level of ordered letters, e.g., "crystalcrystalcrystal," need never be produced by his random efforts, were he to type for eternity. Even more improbable is the meta-meta-level of complexity, in which information is supplied, e.g., "To be or not to be, that is the question." Hence, it is fallacious to assert that since some set of conditions must obtain in the universe, the actual set is in no way improbable or in need of explanation.

[19]John A. Wheeler, "From Relativity to Mutability," in *The Physicist's Conception of Nature*, ed. J. Mehra (Dordrecht: D. Reidel, 1973).

of many different mini-universes which inflated from the original larger Universe.[20] One of the most widely discussed World Ensemble scenarios is Everett's Many Worlds Interpretation of quantum physics, according to which all possible states of a quantum interaction are actualized, the observer himself splitting off into each of these different worlds.[21]

Now it needs to be emphasized that there is no evidence for any of these theories *apart from the fact of intelligent life itself.* But as John Leslie, the philosopher of science who has occupied himself most thoroughly with the Anthropic Principle, points out, any such evidence for a World Ensemble is equally evidence for a divine Designer.[22] Moreover, each of the above scenarios faces formidable scientific and philosophical objections.[23] Wheeler's theory, for example, not only succumbs to the problems generic to oscillating models,[24] but insofar as it posits singularities at the termini of each cycle, it is not even a model of an oscillating universe at all, but of just a series of unrelated worlds. Inflationary models not only face the problems of how to get the inflation started, how to get it to end without excess turbulence, and how to get it to allow galaxy formation, but more importantly they themselves require an extraordinary amount of fine-tuning prior to inflation, so that the appearance of design is not eluded. The Many Worlds Interpretation of quantum physics is so fantastic that philosopher of science John Earman characterizes its postulated splitting of space-time as a "miracle." "Not only is there no hint as to what causal mechanism would produce such a splitting,"

---

[20] A.D. Linde, "The Inflationary Universe," *Reports on Progress in Physics* 47 (1984):925-986.

[21] Hugh Everett, "'Relative State' Formulation of Quantum Mechanics," *Review of Modern Physics* 29 (1957):454-462.

[22] John Leslie, "Modern Cosmology and the Creation of Life," in *Evolution and Creation*, ed. Ernan McMullin, University of Notre Dame Studies in the Philosophy of Religion (Notre Dame: University of Notre Dame Press, 1985), pp. 97-107.

[23] See, for example, the critiques in Quentin Smith, "World Ensemble Explanations," *Pacific Philosophical Quarterly* 67 (1986):73-81; Leslie, "Prerequisites of Life."

[24] Viz., (i) there is no known physics which could cause the universe to oscillate, (ii) the density of the universe appears to be far below the critical level needed to bring about re-contraction, and (iii) the thermodynamic properties of oscillating models reveal that while they have an infinite future, they possess only a finite past. For discussion, see my *The* Kalam *Cosmological Argument*, Library of Philosophy and Religion (London: Macmillan, 1979), pp.122-30, 135-36.

he complains, "there is not even a characterization of where and when it takes place."[25] In fact, Quentin Smith indicts the theory as incoherent, since the many worlds are supposed to exist in a timeless superspace, which is incompatible with the stipulation that they branch off serially as quantum interactions occur.[26]

Objections can be raised against each of the theories proposed for generating many worlds; but even if we conceded that a multiple universe scenario is unobjectionable, would such a move succeed in rescuing us from teleology and a cosmic Designer? This is not at all obvious. The fundamental assumption behind the Anthropic philosopher's reasoning in this regard seems to be something along the lines of

8. If the Universe contains an exhaustively random and infinite number of universes, then anything that can occur with non-vanishing probability will occur somewhere.

But why should we think that the number of universes is actually infinite? This is by no means inevitable, not to mention the paradoxical nature of the existence of an actually infinite number of things.[27] And why should we think that the multiple universes are exhaustively random? Again, this is not a necessary condition of many-worlds hypotheses. In order to elude the teleological argument, we are being asked to assume much more than the mere existence of multiple universes.

---

[25]John Earman, "The SAP Also Rises: A Critical Examination of the Anthropic Principle," *American Philosophical Quarterly* 24 (1987):312.

[26]Smith, "World Ensemble Explanations," pp. 77-78. It is not clear to me why Smith does not think that his own view of the universe as a quantum fluctuation does not succumb to this same objection, since the superspace of quantum geometrodynamics is atemporal. Perhaps he thinks of the superspace as also temporal, but then one is caught in positing time beyond time, which seems incoherent. And even if a temporal superspacetime is coherent, in infinite time some random fluctuation would have spawned an open universe, which would by this time have so expanded as to coalesce with any other universe produced in the superspacetime by a quantum fluctuation, since it has had eternity to do so, thereby eliminating any ensemble of distinct worlds.

[27]The paradoxical nature of the infinite was emphasized by Hackett, *Theism*, pp.194-95, 294, whose exposition was the seed of my own Kalam *Cosmological Argument*, pp. 69-102.

In any case, the move on the part of Anthropic philosophers to posit many worlds, even if viable, represents a significant concession because it implies that the popular use of the WAP to refute teleology in a Universe whose properties are coextensive with the basic features of our universe is fallacious. In order to stave off the conclusion of a Designer, the Anthropic philosopher must take the metaphysically speculative step of embracing a special kind of multiple universe scenario. That will hardly commend itself to some as any less objectionable than theism.

The point is that the Anthropic Principle is impotent unless it is conjoined with a profoundly metaphysical vision of reality. According to Earman, "Some anthropic theorizers seem all too eager to embrace any form of world making that gives purchase to their modus operandi."[28] Why this desperation? John Leslie explains that although the idea of a World Ensemble is sketchy and faces powerful objections, still people think that it *must be correct, for how else could life originate?*[29] But Leslie argues that the God hypothesis is no more obscure than the World Ensemble nor less scientific, since natural laws and initial conditions are not generally taken to be scientifically explicable.[30] A scientist should consider the interpretation of a divine Designer, or else admit that he simply has no personal interest in the only alternative to the World Ensemble is the God hypothesis, so that if we reject the latter we are stuck with the former.[31]

Martin Gardner, quoting physicist Heinz Pagels, says that the Anthropic Principle raises a new mystery:

"How can such a sterile idea," Pagels asks, "reproduce itself so prolifically?"
He suspects it may be because scientists are reluctant to make a leap of faith

---

[28]Earman, "SAP Also Rises," p. 312. He adds, "That anthropic theorists stand ready to make use of any such speculation which proves handy tells us something about their methodology" (Ibid, p. 311).

[29]John Leslie, "Observership in Cosmology: the Anthropic Principle," *Mind* 92 (1983):575.

[30]Leslie, "Cosmology and the Creation of Life," pp. 98, 112.

[31]John Leslie, "God and Scientific Verifiability," *Philosophy* 53 (1978):79.

and say: "The reason the universe seems tailor-made for our existence is that it *was* tailor-made . . . . Faced with questions that do not neatly fit into the framework of science, they are loath to resort to religious explanations; yet their curiosity will not let them leave matters unaddressed. Hence, the anthropic principle. It is the closest that some atheists can get to God."[32]

Similarly physicist Tony Rothman writes:

It's not a big step from the [Anthropic Principle] to the Argument from Design . . . . When confronted with the order and beauty of the universe and the strange coincidences of nature, it's very tempting to take the leap of faith from science into religion. I am sure many physicists want to. I only wish they would admit it.[33]

But if for atheist and timorous theist alike the World Ensemble and Anthropic Principle are functioning as a sort of God surrogate, what is so sad about this situation is that it is so unnecessary. For with the World Ensemble we have already launched our bark out onto the metaphysical deep; if the God hypothesis provides us a surer passage, why not avail ourselves of it? As Leslie reminds us, those who think that "science proper" has boundaries which are easy to fix are becoming increasingly rare.[34]

THE HYPOTHESIS OF DIVINE DESIGN

In any case, the philosopher who is a theist is certainly at liberty *qua* philosopher, if not *qua* scientist, to introduce God as his explanatory ultimate. What objections then might be raised against the theistic hypothesis? No friend of the Anthropic Principle, Earman seems sympathetic to the hypothesis of divine design, but in the end does not

---

[32]Martin Gardner, "WAP, SAP, PAP, & FAP," *New York Review of Books*, (May 8, 1986), p. 23. The quotation from Pagels is from Heinz Pagels, "A Cozy Cosmology," *The Sciences*, (March/April, 1985).

[33]Tony Rothman, "A 'What You See Is What You Beget' Theory," *Discover*, (May 1987), p. 99.

[34]Leslie, "God and Scientific Verifiability," p. 79.

find it compelling because there is no need to adopt a creation theory of actuality, which this hypothesis presupposes:

> If one adopts a creation story of actuality and if one calculates that the probability of creation of a big bang model having the features in question is nil, then no anthropic principle, construed as a selection principle, is going to resolve the problem. The resolution calls rather for something akin to the traditional argument from Design.

> Alternatively, the need for a creation story of actuality and the need to wrestle with improbabilities of actualization can be obviated by treating actuality as a token-reflexive property of possible worlds not unlike the 'nowness' property of instants of time (see Lewis 1986). On this view all possible worlds, including the merely logically possible as well as the physically possible, are all equally 'actual'. No Creator is needed to anoint one of these worlds with the magical property of 'actuality' and the question of why this property was conferred upon a world having the features in question is mooted.[35]

Here we see the metaphysically extravagant lengths to which philosophers seem compelled to go in order to avoid a divine Designer. Earman, while excoriating Anthropic philosophers for their unwarranted postulate of a World Ensemble, shows himself quite willing to go even further, postulating the actual existence of all logically possible worlds. This involves a metaphysical commitment which is so enormous ontologically and so superfluous for explaining modal locutions that most philosophers have dismissed it as science fiction. Indeed, Plantinga has shown that such a theory of actuality entails the outrageous view that I have all my properties essentially, since it is not I, but a counterpart of me, who exists and possesses different properties in other logically possible worlds.[36] In comparison with Earman's commitment, the hypothesis of theism seems modest indeed.

---

[35]Earman, "SAP also Rises," p. 310. Earman's reference is to D. Lewis, *On the Plurality of Worlds* (London: Basil Blackwell, 1986).

[36]Alvin Plantinga, *The Nature of Necessity* (Oxford: Clarendon Press, 1974), pp. 102-20.

Barrow and Tipler also object to the hypothesis of divine design, maintaining that "careful thinkers" would not today "jump so readily" to a Designer, for (i) the modern viewpoint stresses time's role in nature; but since an unfinished watch does not work, arguments based on omnipresent harmony have been abandoned for arguments based on co-present coincidences; and (ii) scientific models aim to be realistic, but are in fact only approximations of reality; so we hesitate to draw far-reaching conclusions about the nature of ultimate reality from models that are at some level inaccurate.[37] But Barrow and Tipler seem unduly diffident here. A careful thinker will not readily jump to any conclusion, but why may he not infer a divine Designer after a careful consideration of the evidence? Point (i) is misleading, since the operations of nature always work; at an earlier time nature is not like an *unfinished* watch, rather it is just a *less complex* watch.[38] In any case, the most powerful design argument will appeal to both present adaptedness and co-present coincidences. Point (ii) loses much of its force in light of two considerations: (a) this is a condition that affects virtually all our knowledge, which is to say that it affects none of it in particular, so that our only recourse is simply to draw conclusions based on what we determine most accurately

---

[37]Barrow and Tipler, *Anthropic Principle*, p. 30.

[38]The response to this objection would also seem appropriate with regard to Earman's proposed satirical antidote to our surprise at the fine-tuning of the universe: "Imagine . . . the wonderment of a species of mud worms who discover that if the constant of the thermometric conductivity of mud were different by a small percentage they would not be able to survive" (Earman, "SAP also Rises,"p. 314). For if our argument has been correct, then, if mud worms possessed self-conscious intelligence, they should indeed be stunned at the fine-tuning requisite for their existence. For even if mud worms were the highest form of life, the delicate balance of conditions necessary for life itself, not to mention the unbelievable complexity involved in an organism so highly developed as a mud worm, remains unaffected by such an attenuation. Indeed, many teleologists argue for the hypothesis of design simply on the basis of a single cell, a gene, or even a DNA molecule, not to speak of organisms so fantastically intricate as a lowly mud worm. (See, e.g., Charles B. Thaxton, Walter L. Bradley, and Roger L. Olsen, *The Mystery of Life's Origin* [New York: Philosophical Library, 1984]; Hubert Yockey, "A Calculation of the Probability of Spontaneous Biogenesis by Information Theory," *Journal of Theoretical Biology* 67 [1977]:377.) The argument based on the existence of intelligent human life simply heaps on the complexity to be explained.

The truth in Earman's argument is the same point made by Deist satires of the teleological argument: the mud worms could not infer that their existence was the target at which the Creator aimed nor that the Creator was some Great Mud Worm. (Cf.

to reflect reality; fortunately, the evidence at issue here is rather concrete and so possesses a high degree of objectivity; (b) Barrow and Tipler do not feel compelled to exercise such restraint when proposing metaphysically speculative but naturalistic accounts of the universe's basic features, for example, their defense of the Many Worlds Interpretation of quantum physics or scenarios for the origin of the universe *ex nihilo*, which leads one to suspect that a double standard is being employed here. Their objections, therefore, seem to have little force.

John Leslie's reservations with the theistic hypothesis are somewhat different: While concurring with the necessity of positing a divine Designer of the cosmos, he nonetheless argues that the ultimate explanation of the order in the universe cannot be God as traditionally conceived. Leslie plumps for what he characterizes as a Neo-platonic concept of God as the creativity of ethical requiredness. That is to say, if I understand Leslie correctly, the universe exists as it does because it *should*; it is morally necessary that a universe of free agents exist. This ethical requiredness of the universe has a sort of creative power to it that makes the world exist. If there is a personal deity, he, too, is the result of this more fundamental principle. Presumably, Leslie calls this conception Neo-platonic because according to that metaphysic the One, which takes the place of Plato's Good, produces being, the first emanation being the *Nous*, or Mind, which in turn produces the world. The God of traditional theism would be like Plotinus's *Nous* and Leslie's God like the ultimate form of the Good.

But why is the traditional concept of God so unpalatable? Leslie's critique on this score is disappointing and surprisingly weak.[39] Proceeding from the Leibnizian question, "Why is there something rather than nothing?" Leslie rejects the answer of God conceived as either a factually or a logically necessary being. For if God is only

---

goal of creation or that it was necessary for God to create this sort of universe in order to produce man [Ernan McMullin, "How Should Cosmology Relate to Theology?" in *The Sciences and Theology in the Twentieth Century*, ed. A.R. Peacocke (Notre Dame: University of Notre Dame Press, 19), pp. 44-45].) But the teleological argument need not be so anthropocentrically construed. It contends merely that the complex order of the universe requires as its most plausible explanation a Cosmic Intelligence which designed the universe. To show that man (or the mud worm) is the goal of creation would require additional arguments, say, the moral argument, or revelation.

[39]See John Leslie, "The World's Necessary Existence," *International Journal for Philosophy of Religion* 11 (1980):207-24.

factually necessary, then He exists logically contingently, albeit eternally, and no reason is supplied for His contingent existence. On the other hand, God cannot be shown to exist necessarily in the logical sense, for when the ontological argument asserts, "It is possible that God exist," this possibility is epistemic only and, hence, does not show that God's existence is logically possible.

But this objection seems confused. If God is merely a factually necessary being, then there are possible worlds in which He does not exist. But then it is logically impossible for Him to exist in all possible worlds, that is to say, it is logically necessary that He exist contingently. But then, assuming that God is the explanatory ultimate in any world in which He exists, it makes no sense to seek a reason for His existence. To demand a reason for His existence is to ask for a logically necessary being which accounts for the fact that God exists. But on this hypothesis, it is logically impossible that there be such a being, for if it were possible such a being would exist in every possible world, including this one, and so God would not be the explanatory ultimate. Hence, if God is a mere factually necessary being, it is logically impossible for there to be a reason for His existence. One need only add that it is wrong-headed to indict a position for not supplying what is logically impossible.

On the other hand, why hold that God is merely factually necessary? The Leibnizian Principle of Sufficient Reason might lead us to reject the concept of God as a merely factually necessary being and hold instead that He is logically necessary. The failure of the ontological argument as a piece of natural theology is irrelevant to the coherence of this conception of God. Leslie correctly points out that when the ontological argument asserts that the proposition "A maximally great being exists" (where maximal greatness entails being omnipotent, omniscient, and morally perfect in every possible world) is possible, there is an ambiguity between "epistemically possible" and "logically possible." To say that such a proposition is epistemically possible is only to say that for all we know it is true. So understood, it makes sense to say, "Possibly a maximally great being exists, and possibly He doesn't." This sense is insufficient for the purposes of the ontological argument. But if we are talking about logical possibility, then to say that the proposition "A maximally great being exists" is possible is to say that He does exist. For if He exists in any possible world, then by definition He exists in all. Thus, if this proposition is possibly true in the logical sense, it is necessarily true. Now I agree with Leslie that the ontological argument seems to fail because all we intuit is that a maximally great being is epistemically possible, but we cannot say if His existence is logically possible. But how is this even relevant to the issue at hand? The coherence of the logical necessity of God's existence does not depend on the success of the ontological argument or our intuitions. It is possible that the ontological argument fails to prove God's existence, and yet for all we know God's existence is logically necessary. Philosophers such as Plantinga, Robert Adams, and William Rowe have defended the coherence of God as a logically necessary being,[40] and Leslie says nothing to impugn this notion. Using the Leibnizian query as his starting point, Leslie ought to conclude to the existence of a being which is by nature such that if it exists in any possible world, it exists in all; such a being must exist in *this* world in order to explain why something exists rather than nothing, and, therefore, in *all* worlds, thereby obviating the need for an explanation of its existence.[41] In this way Leslie's quite legitimate demand for a reason for the existence of something rather than nothing would yield an answer for the universe's existence without requiring one for God's existence, and this without endorsing the ontological argument.

As for Leslie's own alternative conception of God, I think that its lack of explanatory power seems painfully clear. How can there be design without the previsioning of an intelligent mind? Personal agents, not impersonal principles, design things. If one says that the traditional God is a sort of personal demiurge who designed the world, then how can he be produced in being by an abstract principle? Abstract objects such as numbers, propositions, and properties have no spatio-temporal locations and sustain no causal relations with concrete objects. So how does the abstract object posited by Leslie cause a concrete object like God to exist? It thus seems clear that traditional theism is the preferable explanation of the world's design.

---

[40]Plantinga, *Nature of Necessity*, pp. 197-221; Robert Adams, "Has It Been Proved that All Real Existence is Contingent?" *American Philosophical Quarterly* 8 (1971):284-91; William L. Rowe, *The Cosmological Argument* (Princeton: Princeton University Press, 1975), chap. 4.

[41]See the helpful comments by Thomas V. Morris, review of *The Quest for Eternity*, by J.C.A. Gaskin, *Faith and Philosophy* 3 (1986):334.

CONCLUDING REMARKS

Teleologists and Anthropic philosophers enjoy a peculiar "love/hate" relationship: They agree that the delicate balance of cosmological and physical conditions necessary for intelligent life does cry out for some sort of interpretation which will render it intelligible; but they differ radically as to what that interpretation should be. Theistic philosophers view this sensitive nexus of conditions as evidence of wider teleology and therefore indicative of a cosmic Designer. Anthropic philosophers contend that due to the self-selection effect imposed by our own existence we can only observe a limited number of worlds; therefore, we should not be surprised at observing this one. Moreover, if a Word Ensemble exists in which all possible values of cosmological and physical quantities are somewhere instantiated, it follows necessarily that our world with its delicate balance of conditions will also obtain. We have seen, however, that in the absence of the hypothesis of the World Ensemble the reasoning of the Anthropic philosopher, based on the trivial WAP is simply logically fallacious. As for the World Ensemble, there is not only no evidence that such an ensemble of worlds exists, but there are substantive objections against each of the proposed means of generating such an ensemble. In any case, the postulation of a world ensemble is metaphysically extravagant, for it must involve the existence of an infinite number of exhaustively random worlds if one is to guarantee that our world will by chance alone obtain in the ensemble. Theism is certainly no more objectionable than this.

Finally, I should like to say a word concerning the religious value of the hypothesis of divine design as an explanation for the wider teleology we have discovered in nature. As the debate over the Anthropic Principle has spread, it has even taken on literary dimensions, finding its way into the contemporary novel *Roger's Version* by John Updike. When Dale Kohler explains that physicists are proving the existence of God, Roger Lambert, a professor of theology, replies:

For myself I must confess that I find your whole idea aesthetically and ethically repulsive. Aesthetically because it describes a God who lets Himself be intellectually trapped, and ethically because it eliminates faith from religion, it takes away our freedom to believe or doubt. A God you could prove makes the whole thing immensely, oh, uninteresting. Pat. Whatever else God may be, He shouldn't be pat.[42]

Roger's objections, so typical of contemporary theology, reveal fundamental misunderstandings about the revelation of God and the nature of faith. God's handiwork in nature is not a matter of His being intellectually trapped, but of His revelation of Himself to His creation, a self-disclosure which is aesthetically beautiful; as the Psalmist says, "The heavens are telling the glory of God and the firmament proclaims his handiwork" (Ps. 19.1). And the decision to believe in God or not is not so much a matter of *assensus*, but of *fiducia*. The demonstration of His existence on the basis of His created order in no way removes our freedom to trust in ourselves rather than in Him; as Paul wrote, "although they knew God, they did not honor him as God . . ." (Rom. 1.21). The teleological argument, then, if successful, hardly makes belief in God pat.[43] Rather it helps to bring us more quickly to the true crisis of faith.

---

[42]John Updike, *Roger's Version* (London: Deutsch, 1986).

[43]One thinks in this connection of Aristotle's God, who served in his physics and metaphysics as an explanatory principle, but was not an object of religious devotion or worship. Aristotle's conception of deity ought to make quite clear that the postulate of a divine Designer does not settle for us the religious question.

What In The World Is God Doing?

Stephen Bilynskyj

First Evangelical Covenant Church

Lincoln, Nebraska

THE IMPORTANCE OF A THEORY OF PROVIDENCE

The central feature of Stuart Hackett's philosophical work is probably his exposition of the cosmological argument as the basis for a Christian apologetic possessing both persuasive power and rational integrity. *The Resurrection of Theism*[1] presents the cosmological argument as the best case for theism and also presents a case for the epistemological substructure needed by Hackett's version of the argument. *The Reconstruction of the Christian Revelation Claim*[2] recapitulates some of the epistemological and metaphysical argument of *RT*, but its primary aim is to develop a comprehensive case for the "revelation claim" lying at the heart of Christian faith.

It is beyond the scope of this paper to assess Hackett's apologetic project as a whole. I will say that I am impressed by his courageous willingness to paint a broad picture,

---

[1] (Chicago: Moody Press, 1957); 2d ed. (Grand Rapids, MI: Baker Book House, 1982). Hereafter, *RT*.

[2] (Grand Rapids, MI: Baker Book House, 1984). Hereafter, *RCRC*.

setting apologetic arguments within a wholistic understanding of God and the world. In passing, I mention that I believe that the section of the introduction to *RCRC*, entitled "The Development of the Concept of Revelation," deserves further attention for its suggestion that self-revelation is an act not only of God but of every creature: Revelation occurs in varying degrees and occurs in its fullest sense in God.

However, in this paper my concern is with Hackett's clear understanding that an apologetic for the specifically *Christian* revelation claim must deal with the nature of God's interaction with the world He has created. For the Christian (and the ancient Hebrew), one part of God's self-revelation is that He has acted and will continue to act within the world He has created. To assess the claim that such revelation has occurred, it seems to me necessary first to develop a coherent general picture of God's relationship to events within the world. That is, it is crucial to develop some understanding of the notion often called "providence."

Thus I propose, in this paper, to attempt the development of an embryonic notion of providence. I shall try to show that I am operating within a framework of assumptions shared by Stuart Hackett in his apologetic project. However, I believe the end result of my notions of providence may entail some disagreements with Hackett, particularly concerning the nature of miracles.

I need to make it clear that the notion of providence with which I am concerned here is primarily philosophical. So my concern is more with the metaphysical mechanisms of God's activity in the world than it is with theological questions concerning the ends towards which providence directs the world. Moreover, I find it mostly beyond the limits of this paper to deal with the question of providence in relation to the actions of free human agents. I shall only attempt to give some account of God's action in relation to natural agents and/or events in general, realizing that free activity other than God's complicates the matter.

Even within the limits I have set, I believe that an account of God's action in the world has serious ramifications for both Christian understanding and practice. Not only will it have direct bearing on the assessment of revelation claims, especially revealed occurrences of the miraculous, but it will color the way in which one views the nature of petitionary prayer. A Christian's devotional confidence in God's guidance will also be affected by the way God's role in natural events is conceived. It makes a significant difference to faith how one answers the question concerning just what God is doing in the world.

GOD AND SECOND CAUSES

My approach to developing a view of God's relationship to natural agents or events will be to consider a taxonomy of three views concerning God's causal relationship to what have traditionally been called "second causes." This way of looking at things simply sees individual objects in the world as causes bringing about events through a causality which is in some way "secondary" to the causality exercised by God as creator, *i.e.*, as "first cause."

An emphasis on the primacy of the divine causality is, of course, consistent with Hackett's placing of the cosmological argument at the heart of the apologetic enterprise. Likewise, I concur that "the biblical writings regard the natural order itself as continuously sustained in its existence and operation by the operation of an immanent divine agency or causality."[3] Both on philosophical and biblical grounds it is reasonable to speak of God as "first cause."

I must also agree with Hackett that it is necessary to reject a view of providence which emphasizes the divine causality to the *exclusion* of the possibility of any genuine causality within the created world.[4] On such a view, the only genuine agent in any event is God. In the drama of the world, God is the only actor. Second causality, on such a view, simply does not exist. Traditionally, such a view has been called "occasionalism," and Malebranche is usually seen as its classic expositor. Perhaps the most recent defense of an occasionalistic view of providence is to be found in an article by Del Ratsch.[5]

The denial of second causality seems to be prompted by what Alvin Plantinga has called the "sovereignty intuition," that God is in control of all that is and occurs.[6] To allow creatures any causal efficacy of their own appears to limit God's control of events.

---

[3]*RCRC*, p. 322.

[4]Ibid.

[5]"Nomo(theo)logical Necessity," *Faith and Philosophy* 4 (1987):383-402.

[6]See *Does God Have a Nature?* (Milwaukee: Marquette University Press, 1980).

Yet the denial of second causality is strikingly counter-intuitive. We regularly speak of matches causing fires, baseballs breaking windows and sunshine melting snow. Moreover, to deny causal efficacy to creatures makes the world a sham or puppet show which God moves for His own enjoyment. I am convinced that the rejection of genuine created causality is a denigration of the value of creation, a rejection of the biblical statement that the world as created is good. Thus I wish to argue that the concern for God's sovereign control of events may be satisfied within the context of a view of providence which does allow genuine causality to created things.

In the history of philosophy, a view of providence that allows for second causes might be traced to suggestions in the writings of Augustine. Stanislaus J. Grabowski even suggests that Augustine may have held a view of providence much like more sophisticated accounts of second causality to be found in medieval writers.[7] A greater emphasis on second causality in the Middle Ages may be the result of the recovery of Aristotle's philosophy.

In the late Middle Ages, a taxonomy of viable views of second causality appears in the work of Luis Molina (perhaps best known for his concept of "middle knowledge").[8] He sees three basic positions as possibilities. The first is the occasionalistic denial of second causality, which I have already rejected. The second view, which is shared by Molina with Thomas Aquinas, is that God and created things both participate in the production of natural events. That is, for any natural event, both divine causality and the causality of created things is operative. The third view might be termed "Deistic." On this latter scheme, God creates individual things with causal efficacy such that they produce events in the world apart from any divine causal action except the conservation of the individual "natural agents" in existence.[9]

At first glance, the Deistic view recommends itself; it may be the pre-reflective view of most theists. Grabowski feels that the Deistic view of providence is probably

----

[7]*The All-Present God* (St. Louis: St. Louis University Press, 1954), pp. 152-54.

[8]*Concordia liberi arbitrii cum gratiae donis, divina praescientia, providentia, praedestinatione et reprobatione*, Pt. I, Q. 14, Art. 13, Disp. 26. I am indebted to a partial translation and commentary by Alfred Freddoso. Hereafter, *Concordia*.

[9]A more extreme view would, of course, be traditional Deism which holds that not even God's conservation of existence is necessary for the existence and operation of things in the world, once created.

the attitude of many of the Church Fathers before Augustine. Augustine himself may occasionally be interpreted Deistically.[10] The Deistic approach also seems to satisfy the sovereignty intuition. As Creator and Conserver of every causal agent, God may be said to be the primary cause of all that occurs. Every event is brought about either by God or by that which depends on God for its continued existence. A match produces a fire only because God conserves it in existence as the sort of thing that can produce a flame. Thus God is clearly in control of all that occurs, since He determines what will exist and what sort of causal efficacy it will have.

The Deistic view also recommends itself by conforming to our common sense practice of speaking of the causal efficacy or power of individual things in just the way I have been doing. Humean philosophers of science are suspicious of talk of causal powers, but the general outlook of a philosophy of science which deals in causal powers has been rehabilitated by analysis of such powers as dispositional properties of things in the world.[11] I believe that the difficulties surrounding "causal power" understandings of the natural order (noted by Ratsch[12]) are no greater than the difficulties attached to developing a successful account of nature in terms of universal regularities,[13] and causal power views have the advantage of being more in line with our ordinary manner of speaking about natural events.

Therefore, it is no limitation of a Deistic view of providence that it suggests a causal power understanding of the natural order. However, it might be contended that a Deistic view does not afford to God a full measure of honor for and control over what happens in the physical world. His sovereignty requires that God be regarded as the cause of natural events in a more intimate way than is allowed for in the Deistic framework. Such a view makes God, to a certain extent, passive with respect to events in the natural world. He sustains its existence, but its events occur independently of His immediate operation and control. Scripture seems to suggest something more when it attributes

---

[10]Grabowski, *All-Present God*, p. 152.

[11]R. Harre and E.H. Madden, *Causal Powers* (Oxford: Blackwell, 1975).

[12]Del Ratsch, "Nomo(theo)logical Necessity."

[13]Ratsch's own solution to the problem of the description of the natural order is ultimately occasionalistic, though it does include some subtle analysis of the nature of natural law statements.

to God the events and movements of the natural world.[14] It would do more honor to God and ascribe to Him more control to maintain somehow that He not only creates and sustains individual natural things, but that He is involved immediately in the production of natural effects. Thus He would be not only Creator but immediate Cause of all that occurs.

So Molina presents as the only viable view of providence that scheme held, with variations, both by himself and by Thomas Aquinas. On their view, God acts together with natural things to produce natural effects. When fire burns it is true both that fire acts as an agent, with its own power, and that God acts also to produce the effect of burning.

Molina and Thomas differ on just how the causality of God is conjoined with that of natural agents, but they agree that both are active in the production of natural events. They agree in espousing a view of providence which has all the advantages of the Deistic view as well as a stronger notion of God's sovereignty over the natural order. The Latin term for the dual role of divine and natural causality was *concursus*. Thus I would term the view of providence which allows both God and natural things a causal role in natural events a "concurrence" view of providence. Such a view, I believe, is in keeping with Stuart Hackett's own desire both to affirm "an immanent divine agency or causality which pervades the whole of that [natural] order down to its last detail,"[15] and that "This does not mean that contingent entities (persons or things) have no intrinsic causal efficacy of their own."[16]

A CONCURRENCE VIEW OF PROVIDENCE

It remains to examine somewhat just what is meant by a "concurrence" in the production of natural events by both God and natural things. One point should be made clear: concurrence is to be understood as an addition to the creative and sustaining role of the divine power. Thus the Deistic understanding of providence is, in effect, included in a concurrence view.

---

[14]See Job 10:11 and chapters 38 and 39, as well as Genesis 9:13, 14.
[15]*RCRC*, p. 322.
[16]Ibid.

particular. It is, in effect, God's causal action that determines the kind of event produced.

But on Molina's view a greater role is ascribed to the particularity of natural causes. God, in general, concurs with the production of effects in the natural world appropriate to the kinds of causes which exist. When a piece of paper is burned, God's action is not described as "burning the paper," but as a general cooperation with an action particular to fire. The paper burns because it is the particular nature of fire that it consumes paper, not because God executes a particular action of burning.

Now the Molinist position that God's concurrence in natural events is a general rather than a specific action seems to me to have several advantages for the continuing development of a theory of providence. The first advantage I have already touched on: If God's action in a natural event is general and the action of a natural cause in the same event is particular to the kind of cause involved, then there is the beginning of an understanding of the "division of labor" between divine and creaturely causality. Such a division avoids in a more definite way the collapse into occasionalism which appeared in the instrumental picture of concurrence. Natural things remain genuine causes and make a definite contribution to the production of events.

The second advantage of holding God's concurrence to be a general influence is that there is thereby created some room for a plausible solution to the problem of defining God's providential action in relation to the free actions of human agents (and perhaps other sentient, free creatures). The specific character of a free act would depend upon the causal action of the created agent (upon that agent's "volition" or "choice," perhaps), and God's part in the free act would simply be a general concurrence in the production of an event, the specific nature of which is determined by the free created agent. Thus, even in the case of events resulting from free action, God could be said to be the cause of all that occurs, yet without it being required that God *determines* all that occurs. The possibility of such a solution to the question of freedom and providence, in fact, appears to have been Molina's primary motivation for developing his own view of concurrence.

The Molinist solution to the problem of free will also makes some movement possible in another area of the discussion of providence. If we may attribute to God a general resolve to concur with the actions of free creatures, rather than a series of specific decisions to move free creatures to particular actions, then there is a happy resolution to the problem of moral evil in sight. Or, at least, the problem of moral evil is moved to a point where theodicy may begin to offer a reasonable account. That is, while it appears to be difficult to account for a specific decision on God's part to participate in the production of an evil action, it seems plausible (and I believe plausible accounts have been offered) that there could be a good account of a general divine intent to concur with free actions irrespective of their moral nature. Of course, there remains the difficulty that, on traditional notions of omniscience, God knows all the specific results of such a general concurrence with free action. But that is a problem in any scheme of providence, and Molina's view has the virtue of eliminating a specific divine participation in the production of evil acts.

I believe that there is a third advantage to Molinism. A general divine concurrence with natural events allows for the existence of genuine contingency or chance in the natural order. Moreover, genuine contingency is allowed for, but not required. The Deistic view is the only other theory of providence which makes such an allowance. On either an occasionalistic or Thomistic account, God acts specifically to produce each event which occurs. If a genuinely contingent event, to give a simple definition, is taken to be an event which is not determined, either by previous events or by a free agent, then it is difficult to see how such events could occur in the occasionalistic or Thomistic world. The most that could be said is that some events might be contingent from a human epistemic framework. We would simply be unable to *know* the parameters of God's production of such events.

Recent interpretations of quantum theory in physics have seemed to lean toward understanding the indeterminacy of quantum phenomena as a genuine, rather than an epistemic, indeterminacy. That is, certain quantum events, such as the motions of electrons, appear to be genuinely contingent, happening by chance (within certain parameters as defined by quantum theory). Since our current best understanding of the physical world includes genuine contingency, it would behoove us to leave genuine contingency as a live option in any theory of providence.

I have already noted that contingency in the form of free action not determined by God is possible in a Molinist world. If we suppose that God has created some natural things, such as quantum particles, with a power for actions which neither He nor prior events determine, then it seems reasonable to suppose that such indeterminate events will be genuinely contingent as long as God's concurrence with such events is general rather than specific. God would still participate in quantum events, but His participation would take the form of a general consent to the production of *any* event within the parameters of possibilities for such events. Such a scheme would leave us free to regard at least some events in the world as the products of genuine chance.

The possibility of genuine contingency within God's providential activity in the world is suggestive for theodicies concerning *natural* evil. If some natural events happen by chance and are not specifically determined by God, then it is possible that at least some natural events which cause pain and suffering are the results of chance and are *not* the result of any specific action of God. This is, of course, not a solution to the problem of natural evil, even if all evil natural events are the results of chance.[22] As Peter van Inwagen indicates, it simply shows that theodicy will proceed on firmer ground in trying to offer some account of why God created a world in which natural evil is allowed to occur, rather than seeking explanations for the occurrence of specific evils. For if a specific event is the result of chance, then there is, clearly, no explanation for it except a general explanation or reason for a world in which chance events may occur.

Therefore, I maintain, for reasons offered in the second section, that a concurrence theory of providence will best fit our ordinary understandings of the operation of the natural world *and* that such a theory will adequately maintain the theological intuition that God is in sovereign control of all that occurs. In the last section, I have argued that a Molinistic view of concurrence has distinct advantages over other views which seem to lapse into deistic or occasionalistic outlooks. But a difficult question remains.

JUST WHAT IS CONCURRENCE?

The reader would be perfectly correct to note, at this point, that though concurrence has been described as a general, immediate, simultaneous action of God to produce the effect, the exact nature of the divine concurrence remains unclear. What is it that the divine action adds to the production of a natural event over and above the conservation in existence of the cause and the action of the cause itself? I confess that I am not

---

[22]Van Inwagen makes this point clearly in "The Place of Chance in a World Sustained by God," in Thomas V. Morris, *Divine and Human Action: Essays in the Metaphysics of Theism* (Ithaca: Cornell University Press, 1988), pp. 211-235.

entirely satisfied with the best answer I can give to this question, for it seems to bring the concurrence view suspiciously close to the Deistic understanding of providence.

The best description I can give of a Molinist notion of concurrence, beyond what was said in the last section, is that it is a general decision of God to sustain in existence not only natural things and their causal powers, but also the effects produced by natural things. So, in a sense, concurrence is an extension of the divine conservation of all things in existence.

If conservation is understood as a moment by moment continuous creation of all things (not a re-creation, for things surely do not pop in and out of existence), then perhaps it becomes clearer that concurrence may be a kind of conservation of a natural effect. If it is given to a natural cause to be able to produce an effect, it is nonetheless necessary that God, at the same time the effect is produced, will that the effect remain in existence. The effect, at the moment of its production, requires the divine conservation like any other natural thing.

But, it might be objected, causes and effects do not seem to be the same sort of thing. Causes, at least on the scheme I have been working with, seem to be objects, that is, individual substances of some sort. Effects, on the other hand, seem to be better described as events, a much more elusive type of entity. Thus it would appear difficult to understand what conservation of an effect, an event, would amount to.

Now a whole metaphysical can of worms has been opened in the last paragraph. A standard philosophical notion of events (a notion usually connected with Roderick Chisholm) is that events are states of affairs, that is, abstract entities. Such abstract entities become "concretized," or instantiated in the arrangements of actually existing individual things. Thus an event is not, itself, an individual thing. Events exist as abstract entities, that is, as descriptions of arrangements of individual things which may or may not be actually instantiated in the arrangement of the world. It is also possible to develop a conception of events as purely derivative entities. Events exist only insofar as they actually occur in the arrangement of the world. Events have no abstract existence apart from the actual arrangements of individual things.

However, I believe that we can reach a helpful description of an effect without solving the problem of the ontological status of events. I would suggest that an effect can be described as a succession of arrangements of individual things. The simplest way to picture this description of effects is atomistically.[23] We may view the world as an arrangement of "Newtonian" particles existing moment by moment in various arrangements of relative position and velocity and exerting various influences on each other such as attraction, repulsion, and so forth. The atomistic picture is simple, but the notion of arrangement of individual things could be construed in other ways, for example, as an arrangement of quantum entities, Leibnitzian monads, or ordinary objects such as trees, tables, and stones. In the latter cases the description of the relationships which make up the arrangement would be more complex, but it will still be possible to conceive the world at any particular moment as a particular arrangement of individual things.

So, if we describe the world at a given moment, call it T, as an arrangement of all the individual things, then the production of an effect at some future moment, call it T + 1, will simply be the production of a change in the arrangement which existed at T. Since the arrangement of the world is obviously changing constantly as a plurality of effects are produced by a plurality of causes, the arrangement of the world will be different at each successive moment.[24]

I have already noted that God's creative activity is usually construed as a moment by moment conservation of all things in existence. But it is clear that God not only conserves all things in existence at any given moment, but that He also conserves them in existence in their arrangement at that moment. Since that arrangement is constantly changing, God's act of conservation is, in effect, a decision at each moment to conserve a new arrangement of things. God wills not only that each individual thing should exist at a particular moment, but that each thing should exist in all its new relationships with other things. Concurrence, then, is a general decision on God's part to conserve the world moment by moment *along with* all the changes in its arrangement produced by the causal activity of things in the world.

Thus, for any given causal event, God's concurrence in the production of an effect is His general decision not only to conserve in existence the cause and those things upon which it acts, but also to conserve the cause and those things upon which it acts

---

[23] I owe this picture to Peter van Inwagen, "Place of Chance."

[24] I see no *a priori* reason why a past arrangement might not be duplicated at some future moment, but it may be that the nature of time and entropy prevents such duplication. If such a duplication were possible, I do not believe that it affects my argument.

in a new arrangement produced by the cause. This is a general decision to conserve whatever effects are produced by a cause according to the nature of the cause, so that, in the case of quantum particles or free sentient agents, the effect may be one of a number of possible effects.

I believe that my account of concurrence as conservation of effects, which are construed as new arrangements of individual things, is not simply a return to the Deistic view. On the Deistic view God appears to be simply a passive observer of the operations of the world He has created and sustains in existence. The notion of concurrence acknowledges a moment by moment participation by God in the operations of the world by a general decision to sustain the world's existence in each new arrangement as it is produced. Perhaps my account simply reduces concurrence to a refinement of the Deistic view, but if that is the case, it is nonetheless a needed refinement and a corrective to the Deistic view as usually stated.

Thus far, I do not think I have suggested anything about God's providential relationship to the natural order with which Stuart Hackett would not concur. But if the general picture of providence which I have suggested is accepted, there follows what I take to be a fairly simple and satisfying definition of the nature of the divine activity in the production of the miraculous. If God's ordinary providential activity is conservation of individual things and concurrence with the effects they produce, then miraculous activity is the result of a divine decision to produce an effect, or arrangement of the world, which could not or would not have been produced by individual things operating on their own in the sphere of ordinary providence. That is, a miracle is an event beyond the power of natural things, given only God's conservation and concurrence. With such a definition of miracle I am sure that Hackett would disagree.[25] But, of course, a student need not agree with all the views of his teacher in order to acknowledge the enormous debt owed to one who, more than anyone, provided an example of careful thought about things divine. To Stuart Hackett I am so indebted.

---

[25]*RCRC*, p. 322.

Nagel And The Meaning Of Life

Pat A. Manfredi & Donna M. Summerfield

Hamilton College

Many philosophical challenges to the meaning of life contrast the aspirations and strivings of human beings with the lack of value in the world described by science. The following passage from Walter Stace's "Man Against Darkness" represents this challenge:

> . . . for the past three hundred years there has been growing up in men's minds, dominated as they are by science, a new imaginative picture of the world. The world, according to this new picture, is purposeless, senseless, meaningless . . . .
>
> . . . If the scheme of things is purposeless and meaningless, then the life of man is purposeless and meaningless too. Everything is futile, all effort is in the end worthless. A man may, of course, still pursue disconnected ends, money, fame, art, science, and may gain pleasure from them. But his life is hollow at the center.[1]

---

[1] W.T. Stace, "Man Against Darkness" in *The Meaning of Life: Questions, Answers and Analysis*, eds. Steven Sanders and David R. Cheney (Englewood Cliffs, NJ: Prentice-Hall, 1980), p. 40.

Stace's claim appears to be that, given the modern scientific picture of the world, there is no value in the world as it "really" is, independently of the subjective valuings of human beings. Given this scientific picture, there is a conflict between the value we accord to our own valuings and the lack of value accorded to those valuings by the world.

If life's meaninglessness or absurdity results from a clash between our aspirations and reality, then claims that life is absurd presuppose claims about the nature of reality.[2] Our aspirations presuppose that our activities have ends whose value is objective, but the reality is very different. As Bertrand Russell writes:

> Brief and powerless is man's life; on him and all his race the slow, sure doom falls pitiless and dark. Blind to good and evil, reckless of destruction, omnipotent matter rolls on its relentless way; for man, condemned today to lose his dearest, tomorrow himself to pass through the gate of darkness, it remains only to cherish, ere yet the blow fall, the lofty thoughts that ennoble his little day.[3]

If this conflict between our aspirations and reality is the source of the meaninglessness of life, then life might not be meaningless if the world were different. In particular, if God existed and had the nature and purposes that Stuart Hackett claims,[4] challenges such as Russell's and Stace's would lose their force. Both Russell and Stace can be read as saying that human activity is meaningful only if it consists in the pursuit of

---

[2]See Albert Camus, "An Absurd Reasoning" in *Meaning of Life*, pp. 65-75. See also Bertrand Russell, "A Free Man's Worship," in *Meaning of Life*, ed. E.D. Klemke (New York: Oxford University Press, 1981), pp. 55-62.

[3]Russell, "A Free Man's Worship," p. 61.

[4]". . . since God is himself the Ultimate Moral Agent, it is plausible to maintain that in the exercise of that agency he providentially directs the course of events toward the production and progressive development, in moral righteousness, of finite moral selves, and generally as well toward the fulfillment of morally and spiritually significant ends, although always in such a way as not to infringe, in any determining causal way, on the moral freedom of those finite moral selves." (Stuart C. Hackett, *The Reconstruction of the Christian Revelation Claim*, [Grand Rapids, MI: Baker, 1984], p. 89).

goals that have objective and lasting value. But, given an accurate picture of the world, there are no such goals. Hence, human activity is meaningless. Stuart Hackett would respond to this argument by rejecting its second premise. Given the existence and nature of God, there are goals that have objective and lasting value. In this way, many debates about the meaning of life are transformed into debates about the existence and nature of God.

However, Thomas Nagel has argued that our lives are absurd whether or not God exists.[5] Unlike Stace and Russell, Nagel thinks that the absurdity of our lives results from a clash between two different points of view, and not from a clash between our aspirations and reality.

> We cannot live human lives without energy and attention, nor without making choices which show that we take some things more seriously than others. Yet we have always available a point of view outside the particular form of our lives, from which the seriousness appears gratuitous. These two inescapable viewpoints collide in us, and that is what makes life absurd. It is absurd because we ignore the doubts that we know cannot be settled, continuing to live with undiminished seriousness in spite of them.[6]

On the face of things, the theist's response to Stace and Russell will not eliminate the absurdity Nagel finds in our lives, since Nagel insists that the standpoint from which our lives appear to be absurd is available to us whether or not God exists. According to Nagel, the absurdity of life arises because of a clash between two perspectives that we can take on our lives, and not because of a clash between our expectations and reality. From one perspective, we take our lives—our projects and aims—extremely

---

[5]Nagel says this explicitly in "The Absurd," in *Mortal Questions*, (Cambridge: Cambridge University Press, 1979), pp. 16-17. See also the final chapter of *The View from Nowhere,* (New York: Oxford University Press, 1986), where Nagel still attributes the absurdity of our lives to a clash between two different points of view available to us, though he no longer claims explicitly that it makes no difference whether God exists.

[6]Ibid., p. 14.

extremely seriously. From another perspective, we can view everything about which we are serious as arbitrary and open to doubt.[7]

Thus, Nagel challenges our *justification* for regarding our pursuits as valuable rather than challenging the objective value of our pursuits. Even if there is objective value in the world, it seems, we can still question our justification for valuing what we do. Nagel shifts the challenge away from questions about the metaphysical status of value and towards questions about the epistemological status of our valuings. Notice the parallel between these two different challenges to life's meaning and two traditional challenges to our knowledge claims. Just as we may fail to have knowledge either because our beliefs are not true or because they are not justified, so, it seems, our lives may fail to have meaning either because our pursuits are not valuable or because we lack justification for pursuing what we do.

Although Nagel's challenge is an epistemological one, it is not based on the fact that "because we are going to die, all chains of justification must leave off in mid-air." According to Nagel, the justification of most activities comes to a complete and adequate end within an individual's life. Neither my own death nor the death of the universe undermines my justification for taking aspirin when I have a headache.[8] Nagel's point is not that we ask for one more justification in a chain of justifications. Instead,

> We step back to find that the whole system of justification and criticism, which controls our choices and supports our claims to rationality, rests on responses

---

[7]Like Hackett, Nagel would reject the challenge of Russell and Stace, though by rejecting the first premise rather than the second. Nagel believes it is false that "human activity is meaningful only if it consists in pursuit of goals that have objective and lasting value." For one thing, if an activity or product of activity has value, then it does not matter how long it lasts, and, if it lacks value, then it does not help to suppose that it continues forever. See "The Absurd," pp. 11-12. For another thing, from the subjective standpoint, my activities are meaningful, and we have to make a place for the subjective standpoint within our conception of reality; we leave something real out of account if we look at our lives entirely from the objective point of view. See *The View from Nowhere*, p. 7. So Nagel would reject the challenge of Russell and Stace without adopting theism.

[8]See Nagel "The Absurd," pp. 12-13.

and habits that we never question, that we should not know how to defend without circularity, and to which we shall continue to adhere even after they are called into question.[9]

In any case, Nagel's challenge to life's meaning appears quite distinct from earlier challenges. In what follows, however, we shall argue that it is not as distinct as it appears. In particular, we shall attempt to show that although Nagel's conclusion that life is absurd is supposed to follow from epistemological considerations, his argument in fact presupposes a metaphysical picture of the world that is left unjustified.

To begin, it is not obvious that the availability of a standpoint from which we can doubt whether our lives are significant would be enough to make them absurd if our lives really were significant. Consider ordinary cases of absurdity: A man armed only with a sword attacks a group of machine guns;[10] someone gives a complicated speech in support of a motion that has already been passed; you declare your love over the telephone to a recorded telephone message.[11] In each of these cases, there is a conflict between expectations or appearance on the one hand and reality on the other. Sometimes, as in the first case, there is a contrast between the goal being sought and the goal it is possible to obtain given the situation; sometimes, as in the second and third cases, there is a discrepancy between what is believed to be true and what is actually the case. Notice, however, that the absurdity disappears in each of these cases if we imagine a conflict *only* between the seriousness with which each of the individuals engages in the activity and the possibility of bringing that seriousness into question. Suppose, for example, that while declaring your love over the telephone to what you take to be your true love, you suddenly doubt whether there really is anyone on the other end of the line, and you have the unsettling thought that you may be declaring your love to a tape-recorded message. If we suppose that you shake off the doubt and resume your declaring, and if we suppose that, in reality, your true love is listening as you do so, the absurdity disappears. Why should we think that matters are different with our lives? If we suppose, as theists such as Hackett do, that our lives really are

---

[9]Ibid., p. 15.

[10]This is Camus' example in "An Absurd Reasoning," p. 71.

[11]The latter two examples are Nagel's.

significant in the sight of God, then how does the fact that we can step back from those lives and view them *as though* they are insignificant make them absurd?

In Nagel's most recent book, *The View from Nowhere,* he attempts to be more explicit about the nature of the standpoints that generate the absurdity. In order to properly evaluate Nagel's claim that life is absurd, we need to look closely at his characterization of the standpoints (subjective and objective) and ask how a clash between them generates absurdity. The first thing to notice is that there are not merely two standpoints, a subjective one and an objective one, but a continuum of viewpoints whose subjectivity or objectivity is relative to the other viewpoints on the continuum.[12]

The second thing to notice is that in *The View from Nowhere* Nagel gives two *separate* characterizations of what makes one viewpoint more objective than another. On page four he says this:

> To acquire a more objective understanding of some aspect of life or the world, we step back from our initial view of it and form a new conception which has that view and its relation to the world as its object. In other words, we place ourselves in the world that is to be understood. The old view then comes to be regarded as an appearance, more subjective than the new view, and correctable or confirmable by reference to it. The process can be repeated, yielding a still more objective conception.

Two paragraphs later he says this:

> A view or form of thought is more objective than another if it relies less on the specifics of the individual's makeup and position in the world, or on the

---

[12]Nagel never discusses the question of whether there are limits to this continuum, *i.e.,* whether there is such a thing as the most subjective or most objective viewpoint. However, Nagel's claim that there is no viewpoint whose concerns could not be placed in doubt by the backward step of objectification ("The Absurd," p. 16) suggests that he thinks there is no most objective perspective. A theist might argue that God occupies a perspective from which it is impossible to step back, a viewpoint that itself could not become the object of a more objective viewpoint, a view, in effect, from nowhere (everywhere). Although the proposal is interesting, we shall not stop to consider it further.

character of the particular type of creature he is. The wider the range of subjective types to which a form of understanding is accessible—the less it depends on specific subjective capacities—the more objective it is.

These two characterizations do not pick out the same contrast.[13] According to the first characterization, one viewpoint, O, is more objective than another, S, if S is among the objects in O, and, perhaps, if S can be evaluated from the perspective of O. If I am the chair of a college committee and believe that the dean is pressuring me to resign because of differences over a curricular issue, then I achieve a more objective view of the situation if I attempt to step back and see the situation as one in which a particular person is the chair of a committee who also happens to believe that she is being pressured by her dean to resign. This more objective standpoint is a meta-standpoint since it includes among its objects the attitudes that I have about the current situation. Adopting this perspective allows me to detach myself from my own attitudes and to evaluate them to see if they are justifiable.

Nagel's second characterization seems altogether different from the first. Here the characterization is not that of a viewpoint which is more objective than another because it includes that other as its object, but of a viewpoint which is more objective than another because it is accessible to more different "subjective types"[14] than is the other. Thus, if standpoint S is accessible to five different subjective types, and standpoint O is accessible to ten such types, then O is more objective than S. On this scale of subjectivity/objectivity, it seems that my viewpoint as chair of a college committee and

---

[13]Not only do Nagel's characterizations of the subjective and objective standpoints pick out different distinctions, but there is a tendency in each to slide from speaking of subjective and objective standpoints to subjective and objective realities. See Colin McGinn's review of *The View from Nowhere* in *Mind* 96 (1987): 263-72.

[14]Nagel is not particularly clear about what makes two viewpoints members of different subjective types, but see chapter two of *The View from Nowhere*. We think that it is something like the following: Viewpoint S_1 belongs to a different subject type from viewpoint S_2 just in case it is impossible to form a complete conception of the subjective nature of experience from S_1 while one occupies S_2 and vice versa. Some cases are clearer than others; presumably our experiences and those of a bat belong to different subjective types, and perhaps the experiences of our three year old son constitute yet a third subjective type. But do the experiences of men and women belong to different subjective types? What about the experiences of Pat and his twin brother Bill? Nagel gives us no guidance in resolving these questions.

the meta-viewpoint in which *PM* is the chair of the committee are either equally objective (subjective), or worse, that, according to the second characterization, the former is more objective than the latter. That is, if exactly five different subjective types can form a conception of what it is like to be the chair of that committee, we see no reason why any more than five would be able to adopt the respective meta-viewpoint. Moreover, it is not implausible to suppose that creatures with the capacity to form a conception of what it is like to be a committee chair might lack the capacity to adopt the meta-standpoint; many of us are notorious for our inabilities to distance ourselves from the situations we find ourselves in. Given Nagel's second characterization of the objective/subjective distinction, this would appear to have the consequence that the meta-standpoint is less objective than the original.

When Nagel says that the absurdity of life results from the collision of subjective and objective viewpoints within a single person, which of the two characterizations of subjective/objective does he have in mind? Nagel never says. We believe that neither of Nagel's characterizations of subjective versus objective by themselves will serve to explain how a collision of viewpoints could generate absurdity.

To see this, suppose first that life's absurdity emerges from the second subjective/objective contrast. If this were so, a single person would need to conceive of his or her life in at least two distinct ways, one of which was accessible to, say, five subjective types, and the other of which was accessible to perhaps ten subjective types. Assuming for the moment that we can make sense of what this would be like, is there any reason to think that the combination of these two perspectives in a single person would produce absurdity?[15] Suppose that there were a switch on the side of your head that when turned on would enable you to view your life in a way that was accessible both to yourself and to a cockroach, but when turned off would leave your subjective states as they are now (presumably a type which is not accessible to cockroaches).

---

[15]Some philosophical imaginations may be more plastic than ours. In *Practical Ethics*, (Cambridge: Cambridge University Press, 1979), pp. 89-90, Peter Singer proposes a thought experiment in which one has the ability to compare and contrast the conscious experiences of a horse and a normal adult human. Singer suggests that the result of such an experiment should be the recognition that the conscious experience of a normal human has more value than that of a horse. However, even Singer never suggests that the possession of such an ability would make one's life absurd.

Would the fact that this alternative mode of experience was constantly available to you make your life absurd? We do not see why it would.

Again, suppose, to pursue what can only be a rough analogy to the comparison of the experiences of two subjective types, that Donna is reflecting on her role as a mother of a three year old. She can evaluate her performance from the perspective of someone who is an Episcopalian or from the perspective of someone who is both a philosophy professor and an Episcopalian. These two perspectives on her role as a mother may cause her to focus on different aspects of parenting, may affect her evaluation of certain goals that she has for our son, and may bring different values and concerns to the forefront of her thought. However, the possibility of viewing her role from both perspectives does not render her existence as a mother absurd. We conclude that when Nagel says that the absurdity of life results from the collision of subjective and objective viewpoints within a single person, he cannot be thinking of the distinction only in terms of his second characterization.

Is the first characterization, then, able to generate the awareness that life is absurd? Recall that, according to the first contrast, a particular viewpoint is more objective than other viewpoints which it includes as objects. In addition, when we move from one viewpoint to a more objective viewpoint, we come to regard the first "as an appearance, more subjective than the new view, and correctable or confirmable by reference to it." Given this characterization, it is tempting to think of the objective viewpoint as a viewpoint from which values disappear from the world; appearance gives way to reality, and reality excludes values. Nagel cannot think of the objective viewpoint in this way, however. First, if he does, he could no longer claim that our lives would be absurd regardless of what the world were like; his challenge to the meaningfulness of life would collapse into that of Russell and Stace. Second, and more significantly, the subjective viewpoint and its concerns are a part of the world which the objective self considers. A more objective viewpoint includes the more subjective viewpoint as one of its objects, and the more objective viewpoint recognizes that there are pursuits that are genuinely valuable from the subjective point of view. The distinction between the subjective and the objective is not the distinction between appearance and reality because any viewpoint that excludes the subjective viewpoint is a viewpoint that excludes an important part of reality. Nagel criticizes the temptation to label what is revealed from the subjective point of view as "appearance," and therefore as "unreal." Objectivity has its limits, and alone it cannot provide a complete view of reality.[16]

We have been suggesting that neither characterization of the subjective/objective distinction alone is sufficient to generate an argument, different from Stace's and Russell's, that shows life to be absurd. On one hand, the fact that some standpoints from which I view my life may be accessible to more subjective types than other standpoints from which I view my life does not make my life absurd. On the other hand, the fact that I can take a viewpoint on my life from which my initial viewpoint is regarded as mere appearance will generate absurdity only by collapsing Nagel's challenge into Stace's and Russell's.

Still, we think that Nagel does challenge life's meaning in a way different from Stace and Russell, though his characterizations of the subjective/objective distinction do not by themselves enable him to articulate the challenge. In what follows, we isolate four separable steps which together lead to the conclusion that our lives are absurd. Once these steps are isolated, it will become apparent that Nagel's defense of the claim that life is absurd does rest on a particular metaphysical picture, though one different from that of Stace and Russell.

First, suppose that Donna shifts to a more objective viewpoint in Nagel's first sense. Then her new viewpoint will include her former, more subjective, viewpoint among its objects (and not *vice versa*). In order for this shift to a more objective viewpoint to generate absurdity, however, it must reveal something about the more subjective viewpoint that undermines judgments of value made from the latter viewpoint, without making the values recognized from that viewpoint illusory.

Thus, second, suppose that as Donna moves towards objectivity by taking her former viewpoint as itself an object, she recognizes that she is just one subject out of an indefinite number of other subjects and subjective types. In other words, she takes a point of view from which she sees her existence as a particular valuing subject among many (possible and actual) subjects. She still may reasonably deny that her life is absurd, however. By hypothesis, she recognizes the existence of other centers of conscious experience, but that should not lead her to think her life is absurd so long as it is reasonable for her to consider her valuings as more important than the valuings of

---

[16]*The View from Nowhere*, pp. 5-6.

others or so long as her recognition can lead her to place the appropriate value on her own subjective valuings.

Consider an analogy between the absurdity of life and the absurdity of particular desires within life. Suppose that Pat is going to dinner with a group of friends. He would very much like to try the new restaurant in town that specializes in northern Italian cuisine. He discovers that some in the group would rather try the new Indian restaurant and that others want pizza and beer. Does the recognition that there are centers of conscious experience with desires incompatible with his own by itself render his desires absurd? In some cases, there might be reasons for giving the satisfaction of his desires priority. For example, his friends might have promised to take him to whatever restaurant he chose in order to celebrate his birthday. In this case, there is no absurdity in giving the satisfaction of his desires special consideration. Correspondingly, if someone else's birthday is being celebrated, there is no absurdity in giving that person's desires priority. However, even if the desires of all those in the group have roughly equal claims to satisfaction, his desire is still not absurd so long as in recognizing this he adjusts (or could adjust) the importance that he attaches to going to the Italian restaurant accordingly.

What would make Pat's desire to go to the Italian restaurant absurd? We may suppose that he can step back from the situation sufficiently to recognize that his desire is only one among many that are incompatible with his. Suppose, in addition, that the importance that Pat attaches to satisfying his own desire is inappropriate, given the context. For example, suppose that he insists on going to the Italian restaurant even though he recognizes that the person whose birthday it is strongly prefers to go to an Indian Restaurant. This is still not enough to make Pat's desire absurd, we think. We would condemn Pat for being selfish and petty, certainly, but in order for Pat's desire to be absurd, he must in some sense inevitably attach inappropriate importance to the satisfaction of that desire.

By analogy, then, Donna would take step three on the path to recognizing that life is absurd by realizing that the importance she attaches to her desires is utterly inappropriate, and she would take step four by realizing that she inevitably will continue to attach inappropriate importance to her desires. If this is correct, we recognize that life is absurd when we recognize not only that there are a variety of subjective viewpoints whose life projects are to varying degrees incompatible with our own, but also that our subjective viewpoints do not deserve the special consideration we inevitably give them. Careful reading of Nagel indicates that he thinks these two further steps are both necessary and justified.

> . . . to the external view, many different actual and possible subjective values must be acknowledged. Those arising within my life may evoke sympathy, but that is not the same as true objective engagement. My life is one of countlessly many, in a civilization that is also not unique, and my natural devotion to it is quite out of proportion to the importance I can reasonably accord it from outside.
>
> From there I can accord it no more importance than it merits in a global view which includes all possible forms of life and their value on an equal footing.[17]

From an objective view, we recognize many different subjective points of view, ranging from those of people in other cultures to those of bats. We then recognize that we accord far more importance to our own points of view than is warranted (step three). Note especially the justification Nagel gives for taking step three: From an objective viewpoint, we must regard "all possible forms of life and their value on an equal footing." If we do this, we see that our particular concerns are arbitrary and unjustified. At the same time, he thinks, we see that we cannot avoid the "species-ism" to which we shall return in spite of our recognition that it is not justified (step four). We inevitably place a special value on our concerns and projects. When from a more objective viewpoint we recognize the equal claims of uncountably many concerns other than our own and at the same time we recognize that we inevitably treat our own concerns as more worthy of concern than those others, the absurdity of our lives becomes apparent.[18] .

---

[17]Ibid., p. 220. See also pp. 146-47.

[18]For Nagel, the situation is analogous to imagining that sociobiologists had convinced us that all men were determined to adopt sexist attitudes and values, and that nothing short of ceasing to be men could prevent this. The unavoidability of such sexism would not diminish its injustice. Similarly, the objective self's inability to abandon the concerns of the subjective viewpoint does not diminish the arbitrariness of those concerns.

We noted earlier that Nagel's challenge to life's meaning was supposed to be independent of how things stood in the world, and, in particular, it was supposed to be independent of whether or not God exists. It was for this reason that Nagel sought to challenge our *justification* for regarding our pursuits as valuable rather than the objective value of our pursuits. As it turns out, however, Nagel's challenge to our justification for giving our pursuits special consideration does presuppose the truth of a particular metaphysical picture of the world. To be sure, it is not the metaphysical picture of Russell and Stace. There are, after all, real values in Nagel's world. In fact, it is nt the *lack* of objective value in the world, but the *surplus* of subjective (yet real and equal) values that creates the difficulty. Though real, when looked at objectively all of these values are of equal importance. So there is after all a conflict between appearance and reality in Nagel's world, though it is not the conflict between the appearance of values and the reality of a world without values; it is instead the conflict between the inevitable appearance of a world in which our subjective concerns deserve special consideration and the reality of a world in which they do not.[19]

If we are right that a metaphysical picture of a world in which all values deserve equal consideration lies behind Nagel's conclusion that life is absurd, someone might try to escape the conclusion by rejecting the metaphysical picture. For example, someone might claim that values may be ordered objectively. Of course, Nagel might claim in response that any ordering of values is itself merely an appearance from a particular subjective viewpoint. Whereas each subjective viewpoint might have its own ranking of values, from more objective viewpoints these rankings themselves are revealed as arbitrary and unjustified.

In response, we offer a consideration parallel to one Nagel gives in favor of moral realism. Nagel argues that moral anti-realism (that is, the view that denies the objectivity of all values), is not a necessary consequence of adopting the objective

---

[19]Nagel's claim conflicts, not only with some ordinary intuitions, but also with the claims of a variety of ethical theories. Philosophers as diverse as Singer, Nozick, and Rawls would all agree in rejecting it. To cite just one example: Peter Singer, who argues that we must not value the life of any being more than the life of another merely because it is a member of our species, believes it is plausible to suppose that the conscious experience of a normal human has more value than that of a horse. See Peter Singer, *Practical Ethics*, pp. 88-90. See also Robert Nozick, *Anarchy, State and Utopia* (New York: Basic Books, Inc., 1974), pp. 35-47, and John Rawls, *A Theory of Justice* (Cambridge, MA: The Belknap Press of Harvard University Press, 1971), pp. 504-512.

viewpoint. It is a particular substantive claim that should be accepted only if it is more plausible than its denial. In defense of moral realism, Nagel offers the following:

> When we take the objective step, we don't leave the evaluative capacity behind automatically, since that capacity does not depend on antecedently present desires. We may find that it continues to operate from an external standpoint, and we may conclude that this is not just a case of subjective desires popping up again in objective disguise. I acknowledge the dangers of false objectification, which elevates personal tastes and prejudices into cosmic values. But it isn't the only possibility.[20]

The evaluative capacity that continues to recognize the existence of normative values from more objective viewpoints may also continue to recognize the existence of an ordering of values. If, as Nagel suggests, we should resist the temptation to treat all values as illusions of subjectivity, perhaps we should also resist the temptation to treat all orderings of values as illusions of subjectivity. From a subjective point of view we accord different values to different subjective types. This ordering may remain when we adopt a more objective viewpoint. Here, too, there is a danger of false objectification, but again, it is not the only possibility.[21]

If we reject Nagel's assumption that all subjective viewpoints and their corresponding values are objectively equal, we can allow that there may be objective reasons for taking the concerns of some subjective types more seriously than we take the concerns of other subjective types. An individual may be justified in her claim that, if she had the choice, it would be objectively reasonable to pursue her life rather than that of a cockroach; somewhat more controversially, an individual may insist that, even if she had the choice, it would be objectively reasonable to pursue her life rather than that of a chimpanzee. No doubt much depends upon how we define "subjective types." The more finely we discriminate subjective types, the more controversial and

---

[20]*View from Nowhere,* p. 143.

[21]Many of the arguments that Nagel discusses on pages 138-149 concerning the objective existence of values can be adapted to apply to the question of whether or not there is an objective ordering of values.

problematic become the resulting claims about the relative values of different subjective types.[22]

There are various ways of ranking the value of different subjective types. Some versions of theism suggest one way. The Absolute Personhood of God is at the top and our own personhood, as creatures in the image of God, determines our position on that hierarchy. Exactly where on the scale other members of creation fall relative to us is not a simple matter. But every created thing has a value by virtue of its relationship to God. As stewards of God's creation, we are to give each part of God's creation the consideration it deserves. This is no simple task, and, almost inevitably, we err either by underestimating the value of other parts of the created order or by overestimating our own value.

Would this theistic hierarchy or any such hierarchy of values eliminate the absurdity Nagel attributes to our lives? Not necessarily. In such a world it would still be possible, indeed common, to attach more importance to our subjective concerns than they deserve (step three). Nevertheless, Nagel's blanket justification for taking the third step would disappear, since it would simply be false that from an objective viewpoint, we must regard "all possible forms of life and their value on an equal footing."

Even given a hierarchy of values, surely not every concern of a person ought objectively to be taken more seriously than every concern of a creature of a "less valuable" subjective type. Consequently, there would be something absurd in the fact that we regularly attach less importance to the survival of an endangered species than to the desires of those who choose to wear the furs of such species. Again, even given a hierarchy of values, surely not just any concern of a person ought objectively to be taken as seriously as any other concern of a person. Consequently, there would be something absurd in the fact that we regularly attach less importance to the needs of some persons for food and shelter than to the wishes of others for delicacies and summer homes.

---

[22]For example, a woman might claim that the lives of men and women constitute different subjective types, that the lives of women are objectively of higher value than the lives of men, and thus conclude that it is objectively reasonable to pursue her life rather than that of a man. Of course, this latter example seems to be a clear case of false objectification, and, notoriously, human beings are tempted to accord themselves and their "kind" more value than they objectively deserve, but we can recognize this very real danger without going to the opposite extreme.

It may be that we can eliminate whatever absurdity such cases generate by re-ordering our priorities. But is such re-ordering always possible, and, if not, will our lives remain to some degree absurd despite our best efforts? For example, granting that persons are objectively more valuable than mice, the fact that we inevitably put the concerns of persons above those of mice will do nothing to show that our lives are absurd. Still, we undoubtedly will put the concerns of ourselves, our friends, and our children above those of other persons, in spite of the fact that no one person is objectively more or less valuable than any other. It is simply unreasonable to expect that we will actually succeed in valuing every equally valuable person to the same degree. So, it seems, we are stuck with some arbitrary valuings, no matter how objective values themselves may be.

We are not convinced that the remaining arbitrariness would unavoidably generate absurdity, for two reasons. First, to display more concern for one person than for many other equally valuable person seems no less rational than arbitrarily choosing one can of tomato soup from a shelf full of equally desirable cans of tomato soup. In fact, if I want a can of Campbell's tomato soup, it would be irrational to demand a reason for choosing one particular undented can of Campbell's tomato soup over other particular undented cans of Campbell's tomato soup. Of course, there are obvious disanalogies between persons and soup, but, if anything, the disanalogies help our case. For example, persons often have less choice about who they are in the best position to care for than about which can of soup to buy.

Second, we suspect that much of the remaining tension stems from the fact that most of us care for our closest friends and our children in part because they are *ours*. In other words, we care for them not only because they are valuable in themselves and because we are in a better position to care for them than we are to care for others, but also because we think, mistakenly, that they *belong* to us, that they redound to our credit, or that we can somehow live beyond our years through them. In other words, our concern for them is often *egocentric*. Of course, egocentricity is an extremely common characteristic of human beings, but it is not inevitable. As Nagel himself points out, an egocentric attitude is not the only attitude we can and do take towards particular things.

... there is an attitude which cuts through the opposition between transcendent universality and parochial self-absorption, and that is the attitude of nonegocentric respect for the particular. It is conspicuous as an element in aesthetic response, but it can be directed to all kinds of things, including aspects of one's own life. One can simply look hard at a ketchup bottle, and the question of significance from different standpoints will disappear. Particular things can have a noncompetitive completeness which is transparent to all aspects of the self. This also helps explain why the experience of great beauty tends to unify the self: the object engages us immediately and totally in a way that makes distinctions among points of view irrelevant.[23]

This is all Nagel says about the possibility of "nonegocentric respect for the particular," except to express doubt about whether we could sustain this kind of attitude consistently.

It would require an immediacy of feeling and attention to what is present that doesn't blend well with the complex, forward-looking pursuits of a civilized creature. Perhaps it would require a radical change in what one did, and that would raise the question whether the simplification was worth it.[24]

Though Nagel speaks of nonegocentric respect for a ketchup bottle, what he has in mind seems similar to a picture of human interaction with others and the world held up as an ideal by many religious thinkers. If we accept a hierarchy of values, we may non-arbitrarily replace "a ketchup bottle" with "another person," and then the picture seems even more familiar as a religious ideal. In *Notes from the Underground*, Dostoyevsky has given us a powerful illustration of such an attitude in the character of Liza:

But, at this point, a very strange thing happened.

I was so used to imagining everything happening the way it does in books and visualizing things falling somehow into the shape of my old

---

[23]*View from Nowhere*, pp. 222-23.

[24]Ibid., p. 223.

daydreams that at first I didn't understand what was going on. What actually happened was that Liza, whom I had humiliated and crushed, understood much more than I had thought. Out of all I had said, she had understood what a sincerely loving woman would understand first—that I myself was unhappy.

. . . Suddenly she was standing, and in an irresistible impulse, with her whole being drawn toward me but too shy to take a step forward, she stretched her hands out to me. I couldn't stand it any longer . . . .[25]

Liza, the prostitute, sees clearly and responds with "nonegocentric respect for the particular," in this case for a particular person who has just treated her despicably.

Nagel is right that most of us, most of the time, do not display nonegocentric respect for particulars in the way illustrated by Dostoyevsky's Liza. Nevertheless, some of us do succeed, some of the time, and that is enough to show that even the tension that remains after all the moves made earlier have been made is not quite an inevitable feature of our normally all-too-egocentric lives.

[25]Fyodor Dostoyevsky, *Notes from Underground, White Nights, The Dream of a Ridiculous Man, and Selections from The House of the Dead,* trans. Andrew R. MacAndrew, A Signet Classic (New York: New American Library, 1961), p. 197.

Euthyphro And His Kin:
The Kantian Dilemma
For Divine Command Morality

Mark Linville

University of Wisconsin at Madison

According to Kant's Principle of Autonomy, imperatives are *categorical* if and only if they are expressions of universal laws legislated by pure practical reason. In this way, the agent is both lawgiver and subject, in that the moral law proceeds from the rational nature of the agent himself. According to Kant, any form of *heteronomy*, that is, any system of morality in which the agent is "subject only,"[1] can impose *hypothetical* imperatives at best. This is because in all such systems, duty is not to be obeyed for its own sake, but as a means to some further end.

> If the will seeks the law which is to determine it anywhere else than in the fitness
> of its maxims to its own universal legislation, and if it thus goes outside itself
> and seeks this law in the property of any of its objects, heteronomy always

---

[1] Immanuel Kant, *Foundations of the Metaphysics of Morals,* trans. Lewis White Beck (Indianapolis: Bobbs-Merrill, 1959), 2. 433.

results. For then the will does not give itself the law but the object through its relation to the will gives the law to it. This relation, whether it rests on inclination or on conceptions of reason, only admits of hypothetical imperatives: I should do something for the reason that I will something else.[2]

It is this consideration that leads Kant to dismiss divine command morality, or what he calls the "theological conception" of ethics. Kant divides all forms of heteronomy into those that are empirical and those that are rational. The former category would include all theories which employ a hedonistic theory of value, as well as those that are based upon moral feeling or sentiment. He rejects these as lacking the needed universality for moral foundations because they are derived from particular tendencies and accidental features of human persons. That is, sources of happiness and the objects of moral sentiment are often idiosyncratic, differing from individual to individual, and a minimal requirement for the moral law is that the foundation upon which it rests must be some feature universally shared by mankind. Most importantly, any imperatives derived from these will be merely hypothetical and never categorical. Hedonistic moral principles such as "one's own happiness" subvert rather than establish morality because of their appeal to inferior motives for dutiful actions. Indeed, such motives may be equally operative in actions that are actually *contrary* to duty.

This principle supports morality with incentives which undermine it and destroy all its sublimity, for it puts the motives to virtue and those to vice in the same class, teaching us only to make a better calculation while obliterating the specific difference between them.[3]

Thus, if the principle of one's own happiness is taken as the supreme moral principle, virtuous and vicious actions are one in essence, as they proceed from the same principle, and any effects, good or ill, will be merely accidental properties of those actions.

Among the rational forms of heteronomy, Kant includes an "ontological concept of perfection" and the theological concept. The former is an abstract notion of perfection which is held out as an ideal, from which we derive our notions of duty. But

---

[2]Ibid., 2. 441, 442.
[3]Ibid., 2. 443.

this concept is either empty, and therefore useless for determining our duty, or, in case it does have a specific content, such content is actually derived from our own conceptions of morality, in which case morality has its source in human autonomy in the first place.

But even with these criticisms of the ontological conception of perfection, Kant holds that it is better than the theological concept which derives morality from a perfect divine will.

> It [the ontological concept] is better not merely because we cannot intuit its [the divine will's] perfection, having rather to derive it only from our own concepts of which morality itself is foremost, but also because if we do not so derive it (and to do so would involve a most flagrant circle in explanation), the only remaining concept of the divine will is made up of the attributes of desire for glory and dominion combined with the awful conceptions of might and vengeance, and any system of ethics based upon them would be directly opposed to morality.[4]

Here, then, is Kant's objection to divine command morality. Excluding subproofs and allowing for some rearrangement, Kant's argument may be outlined as follows:

A1. Either the concept of the divine will includes the idea of moral perfection or it does not.

A2. If the concept of the divine will does not include the idea of moral perfection, then there is no *moral* obligation to obey the divine will.

A3. If there is no moral obligation to obey the divine will, then the divine will cannot be the source of moral obligation.

A4. If the concept of the divine will *does* include the idea of moral perfection, then the source of that idea is in our own concepts of morality.

---

[4]Ibid., 2. 444.

A5. But if the idea of the perfection of the divine will has its source in our own concept of morality, then the concept of a most perfect divine will cannot be the source of moral obligation.

A6. Therefore, whether the concept of the divine will includes or excludes the idea of moral perfection, it cannot be the source of moral obligation.

Kant's reasoning for propositions (A2)-(A3) involves the supposition that God must have a *moral right* to demand our obedience in order for His commands to constitute moral obligation. And God can have a moral right to demand our obedience only if He is morally good Himself. Thus, God's own moral goodness is a necessary condition of His commands constituting our moral obligation. For suppose we held that we *ought* to obey God's commands, but, for all we know, God is not morally good. What can be said in answer to the question of *why* we ought to obey the commands of God? To what attributes of God may we appeal to ground this obligation? As Kant sees it, all that remain are the concepts of God's demand for absolute obedience, His threat of punishment on all those who do not meet that demand, and His ability to carry out that threat with a vengeance. But then the answer to the question of why we ought to obey the commands of God will reduce to merely prudential considerations which are, in turn, governed by the principle of self-love or one's own happiness. And, again, quite contrary to establishing morality, Kant thinks such a principle actually destroys it. This observation rests upon Kant's first proposition of morality, namely, "to have moral worth an action must be done from duty."[5] To do an action *from* duty is to perform that action solely *because that action is right.*

Thus, in order for divine command morality even to qualify as a contender for the status of an ethical theory, it must be possible to say that our reason for obeying the divine will is simply because it is *right* to do so. But apart from divine goodness, such obedience is reduced to the status of a means for obtaining some desirable state of affairs. And this, again, is to say that the imperative to obey the will of God is hypothetical and not categorical, and thus not a moral imperative.

---

[5]Ibid., 1. 400.

> The will in these cases never determines itself directly by the conception of the action itself but only by the incentive which the foreseen result of the action incites in the will—that is "I ought to do something because I will something else."[6]

Thus, in order for obedience to God to be good in itself and thereby constitute moral obligation, there must be something about God such that it is right to obey Him. Divine goodness is therefore a necessary (though not sufficient) condition for the divine will's constituting moral obligation.

But this leads us to the other disjunct in Kant's argument, represented by propositions (A4)-(A5). To put it most simply, in order for us to know that the divine will is *morally perfect* and therefore meets a necessary condition for being the source of moral obligation, we must *first* know what it *means* to be morally perfect, and *then* predicate that quality to God. But if the moral perfection of God must be explained by reference to our own moral concepts, then it cannot be the case that our moral concepts are explained by reference to the moral perfection of God. This is the "flagrant circle" to which Kant refers. The divine command moralist seems to want to hold that the divine will is the sole source of our moral concepts such that apart from a knowledge of the divine nature, we would have no concept of moral perfection. But in order for him to know that the divine will qualifies as such a source, he must know that the divine will is morally perfect. This argument is operative in the following passage:

> Nor could one give poorer counsel to morality than to attempt to derive it from examples. For each example of morality which is exhibited to me must itself have been previously judged according to principles of morality to see whether it is worthy to serve as an original example, i.e., as a model. By no means could it authoritatively furnish the concept of morality. Even the Holy One of the Gospel must be compared with our ideal of moral perfection before He is recognized as such; even He says of Himself, "Why call ye Me (whom you see) good? None is good (the archetype of the good) except God only (whom you do not see)." But whence do we have the concept of God as the highest good?

---

[6]Ibid., 2. 444.

> Solely from the idea of moral perfection which reason formulates *a priori* and
> which it inseparably connects with the concept of a free will.[7]

The logical force of Kant's argument here is that, quite contrary to the claim that
morality is dependent upon religion, just the reverse is true: Religion is dependent upon
morality. For in order to know that God is worthy of worship and obedience, there must
be some standard by which we evaluate Him, and, in fact, that standard is found in
human autonomy.

It should be quite obvious by now that the above disjunctive argument (A1-A6) is
a Kantian version of the *Euthyphro Dilemma*. This dilemma threatens the theist with
two perilous horns. The first of these might be called the *"arbitrariness"* horn. This is
the problem that follows from affirming the first alternative of the Euthyphro question,
namely, that things are good solely because God wills them. If good things have their
goodness solely in the fact that God wills them, then their goodness is not a quality
possessed by them. Rather, it consists in their relation to God's will. Nothing is either
inherently good or inherently evil. But were this the case, there could be no *moral
reason* for God's willing one thing over another. His *will* would be, by definition, the
ultimate moral criterion, so that there could not be any more ultimate criteria to
determine it. This was the view of John Calvin, who was willing to sacrifice even clear
thinking to what he regarded as a high view of the sovereignty of God. Calvin holds
that it is "wicked to investigate the causes of God's will":

> For His will is, and rightly ought to be, the cause of all things that are. For if it
> has any cause, something must precede it, to which it is, as it were, bound; this
> is unlawful to imagine. For God's will is so much the highest rule of
> righteousness that whatever he wills, by the very fact that he wills it, must be
> considered righteous. When, therefore, one asks why God has so done, we must
> reply: because he has willed it. But if you proceed further to ask why he so
> willed, you are seeking something greater and higher than God's will, which
> cannot be found.[8]

---

[7]Ibid., 2. 409.

[8]John Calvin, *Institutes of the Christian Religion* 3. 23. 2.

Although Calvin would not like to hold that this implies that God's will would be *arbitrary* given such a view of the primacy of His will, it is difficult to see how we can conclude anything else. For, by definition, if God wills things without having any *reasons* for so willing, then His will is arbitrary.

Two serious problems plague such a view—only one of which is emphasized by Kant. The first of these is that if there is no moral reason for God's choosing to issue one set of commands over another, then there is seemingly the very real possibility, in this world or another, that God could issue commands that are the moral opposites of what He, in fact, wills now. Thus, presumably from the same concern for the sovereignty and aseity of God, William of Ockham simply bit the bullet:

> The hatred of God, theft, adultery, and actions similar to these according to the common law, may have an evil quality annexed, in so far as they are done by someone who is obligated by a divine command to perform the opposite act. But as far as the sheer being in these actions is concerned, they can be performed by God without any evil condition annexed; and they can even be performed meritoriously by an earthly pilgrim if they should come under a divine precept, just as now the opposite of these in fact fall under a divine command.[9]

Note that Ockham explicitly refers to the "evil quality" of certain actions as being "annexed" to those actions. Again, on such a view, moral qualities are not inherent in actions themselves but are merely relational, the one important *relatum* being the command of God. As will be discussed later, Kant held that God, if He exists, necessarily acts in accordance with the moral law, which effectively rules out such states of affairs as imagined by Ockham. Thus, Kant never brought out this feature as a problematic implication of the voluntarist version of divine command morality.

The other problem said to arise for the theist who affirms the first alternative of the Euthyphro question is that we are left with no informative content to the proposition "God is good." If "goodness" is solely a function of a thing's being in accordance with

---

[9]William of Ockham, *On the Four Books of the Sentences* Bk. 2. Q. 19, in Janine Marie Idziak, *Divine Command Morality* (New York: Edwin Mellen Press, 1979).

the will of God, then to say that God is good can mean no more than "God does what God wills." Thus, Stephen Davis argues:

> The word "good" is being used in an unusual way—so much so that we have no clear understanding of the sentence "God is good." We can understand what it is for Jones to be good—Jones is good if and only if Jones does what God wills that Jones do. But in what sense is God good? If and only if God does what God wills? But this is surely unsatisfactory. We certainly cannot understand the word "good" in the sentence "God is good" in the same way we understand it in such sentences as "Jones is good." For Jones is not good if Jones robs, murders, and lies, but on the view under consideration God is good no matter what he does. It turns out, then, that "God is good" is no more informative a sentence than "God is God."[10]

This lack of analogy between the commonly understood meaning of the term "good" and the meaning of the word when applied to God precludes the possibility of one's worshiping and obeying God due to any "moral" quality found in Him. Davis continues with a second observation, which is based upon the implications of the first. He writes that the Ockhamite view

> . . . allows for the possibility that God is a being whom we have no moral reason to worship. Why should we worship him if he is not morally good in at least a roughly similar way (though to an infinitely exalted degree) as are morally good human beings? Of course there is nothing in Ockham's view that requires its defenders to say that God actually wills robbery, murder, and lying—it only requires them to say that even if God willed such things he would still be good. But this view seems seriously problematical. Since on Ockham's view God's will is always free, that is, God can will robbery and murder, I would argue that if God willed such things he would no longer be morally good (as I understand the term). Consequently, I would have no moral reason to worship him.[11]

---

[10]Stephen T. Davis, *Logic and the Nature of God* (Grand Rapids, MI: Wm. B. Eerdmans, 1983), p. 91.

[11]Ibid., p. 92.

This is obviously the Kantian point emphasized above. In order to obey and worship God for any moral reason, we must first know that God is morally good. Otherwise, such obedience is merely prudential: Such worship is a matter of groveling. Thus, C. S. Lewis observes:

> If God's moral judgment differs from ours so that our "black" may be his "white," we can mean nothing by calling Him good; for to say "God is good," while asserting that His goodness is wholly other than ours is really to say that "God is we know not what." And an utterly unknown quality in God cannot give us moral grounds for loving or obeying Him. If He is not (in our sense) "good" we shall obey, if at all, only through fear—and we should be equally ready to obey an omnipotent friend.[12]

Kant's observation of the nature of obedience to a divine will stripped of moral perfection is, then, identical to the latter of the two above implications of the voluntarist position of the Euthyphro question. But if this observation corresponds to certain implications of the "arbitrariness" horn of the Euthyphro dilemma, Kant's reference to the "flagrant circle" is analogous to the other horn of the dilemma—what we will here call the "*autonomy*" horn. This horn consists of the implications of the theist's embracing that second alternative of the Euthyphro question, namely, that God wills things because they are good. Here the argument is that if God wills things *because* they are good, then they are good already, logically independent of His willing them. This seems to presuppose that there is some Platonic criterion, distinct from and perhaps even "superior to" God to which He looks for guidance in His willing, much as Plato's demiurge looks to the Forms to turn chaos into a cosmos. But if this is the case, then where is the original claim that morality depends upon the will of God?

There is a slight and subtle distinction between Kant's argument for autonomy and the original force of this horn of the Euthyphro. The distinction becomes most apparent when we begin an attempt to answer the dilemma presented in the Euthyphro. So suppose we do just that.

Perhaps we can find safe passage through the horns of the dilemma by affirming the Anselmian concept of God as a maximally perfect being. If God is defined as the

---

[12]C.S. Lewis, *The Problem of Pain* (New York: Macmillan, 1962), p. 37.

greatest conceivable being, then this can be held to *entail* God's moral perfection. On this account, God is *essentially* morally perfect or necessarily good because goodness is a part of His very nature as God. Does this give us the desired results? At first blush, it may seem that it does. For in this case, we have ruled out the arbitrariness of the voluntarist position. If God is necessarily good, understood *de re*, then there is no world in which God wills evil, and so we seem to have ruled out the arbitrariness problem altogether. The theist can merely point out that God necessarily wills in accordance with His nature. And the theist is also seemingly free of the danger of the second horn. After all, on this account, *God Himself* is the criterion. Thus, although it must be admitted that God wills things because they are good, their goodness is not a matter of their participation in some Platonic criterion of the Good; rather it consists in the fact that they are in accordance with certain features of God's own nature. Thus, the divine nature itself, and not merely the divine will, is taken to be the criterion. Have we not, then, solved the problem merely by such an appeal to essential perfection? It seems not. For this is where Kant's criticisms take over.

Kant argues that we must know that the divine will is good before we know that it is worthy of our obedience. The divine command moralist may think that he is obliging Kant by defining the goodness of the divine will by reference to the divine nature. But this merely delays the inevitable. For everything Kant has to say about our knowledge of the moral qualities of the divine will is directly applicable to our knowledge of the moral qualities of the divine nature itself. Thus, we define goodness in terms of "that which is in accordance with the nature of God." And this works for the purpose of evaluating the divine will. But is the nature of God "good"? We have the same dilemma. Either we cannot give any meaningful content to the "goodness" of the divine nature, or that content has its source in our own moral concepts. Either "God is good" means something roughly akin to "God is, by nature, in accordance with God's nature," which tells us nothing, or we are importing our notion of goodness from elsewhere. And if either is the case, the very logic of the situation rules out God's nature as being the ultimate moral criterion.

What the divine command moralist needs, then, is a way of affirming the goodness of God without thereby impaling himself on the autonomy horn of the Euthyphro. I think such a way is open to the theist, and some of the resources for such a solution are provided by Kant himself.

The mere affirmation of God's essential perfection does not solve the problem posed by the Euthyphro dilemma, but I think it is a step in the right direction. In fact, I think it can be shown that, beyond Kant's insistence that God's moral perfection is a necessary condition for the theological concept of ethics, God's *essential* moral perfection is also a necessary condition. Thus, any view holding that God is contingently morally perfect, or that there is some world in which God does evil, can be shown to be incompatible with any theory which can rightly claim that God's nature or God's will is the ultimate moral criterion. Divine command morality is not an option for the contingent perfectionist.[13] Thus, I propose that, in attempting to provide a plausible answer to Kant's objection, we begin by affirming that God is essentially perfect and that His perfect *nature* is the source of moral obligation rather than His will alone.

But, again, although essential perfection is a necessary condition for a coherent account of divine command morality, it is by no means a sufficient condition. Kant himself provides us with as clear an example as can be imagined of a theory that holds essential perfection but rejects divine command morality. As mentioned above, Kant held that God must necessarily act in accordance with the law. There are at least two elements that work together in Kant's view on divine benevolence.

The first has to do with Kant's view of the nature of morality itself. Morality, for Kant, is grounded in pure reason alone. It is the expression of the practical side of reason. To be immoral is to be irrational. Kant thinks that if there is any being who is

---

[13]The argument for this conclusion is complex, and a thorough presentation would take us well beyond the purpose of the present paper. Essentially it hinges on the observation that if there is any world in which two objects are distinct, then they are distinct in every world in which they exist, which is to say that, necessarily, they are not identical. If there is a world W in which God does evil (and we do not take this to be merely an expression of the voluntarist's position that there is a world in which God does *what is regarded as evil in the actual world*), then, in that world, there is some ultimate moral criterion against which God is measured and found wanting. But if this is the case, then God is distinct from the ultimate moral criterion in W. But if He is distinct from that criterion in W, then He is necessarily distinct from the ultimate moral criterion. But this is just to say that, necessarily, God is not the ultimate moral criterion. This argument calls for refinement, which involves running it through both the *"Divine Will"* and the *"Divine Nature"* versions of theological ethics. The resources for this argument (as is the case with a host of other subjects) may be found in Alvin Plantinga, *The Nature of Necessity* (Oxford: The Clarendon Press, 1974).

God, then that being is necessarily perfectly rational and, hence, cannot fail to act in accordance with moral duties. The fact that God is good of necessity is merely a function of the fact that God is perfectly rational by nature.

> Since reason is required for the derivation of actions from laws, will is nothing else than practical reason. If reason infallibly determines the will, the actions which such a being recognizes as objectively necessary are also subjectively necessary. That is, the will is a faculty of choosing only that which reason, independently of inclination, recognizes as practically necessary, i.e., as good.[14]

Thus, quite simply, in God's case, reason infallibly determines the will, and so those actions that are recognized as objectively necessary are also subjectively necessary, which is to say that God necessarily wills in accordance with the moral law.

Whereas the first element has to do with God's perfect rationality, the second involves God's "perfection" or completeness. Kant holds that every finite rational being has the desire for happiness. But this desire for happiness is limited to *finite* rational beings.

> To be happy is necessarily the desire of every rational but finite being, and thus it is an unavoidable determinant of its faculty of desire. Contentment with our existence is not, as it were, an inborn possession or a bliss, which would presuppose a consciousness of our self-sufficiency; it is rather a problem imposed upon us by our own finite nature as a being of needs. These needs are directed to the material of the faculty of desire, i.e., to that which is related to a basic subjective feeling of pleasure or displeasure, determining what we require in order to be satisfied with our condition.[15]

This desire for happiness is peculiar to rational creatures that are also "beings of needs." Because we are finite and dependent, we lack self-sufficiency and contentment. Thus,

---

[14]*Foundations* 2. 413.

[15]*Critique of Practical Reason*, trans. Lewis White Beck (Indianapolis: Bobbs-Merrill, 1956), 1. 1. 25. See also *Foundations*, 2. 416.

certain conditions must be met in order to achieve these as ends. But, as is often the case, the desire for these conditions of our own happiness can conflict with the moral law. It is when we fulfill these desires, acting on selfish inclinations rather than obeying the moral law that we act immorally.[16]

But God is altogether self-sufficient. He is not finite, dependent, or a being of needs. God lacks the desire for happiness. And lacking this desire, He lacks any inclinations that could conflict with the moral law. God has a "holy will," "a will incapable of any maxims which conflict with the moral law."[17] Thus, God's very nature is in agreement with the moral law.

For our purposes, the most important point about Kant's view here is a certain conclusion which he thought followed from the fact that God necessarily acts in accordance with the moral law. According to Kant, if God's *nature* is such that He *cannot fail* to act in conformity with the law, then He is not subject to duty or obligation. Kant's own reason for holding this view is that one's duty is that action which is done out of pure respect for the moral law. And respect for the moral law always operates in such a way as to check those inclinations that are contrary to the moral law. On Kant's view, if one is so constituted as to have one's will always in perfect agreement with the law, then that person's actions in accordance with law are not done out of respect for the law, and thus not out of duty.

> For men and all rational creatures, the moral necessity is a constraint, an obligation. Every action based on it is to be considered as duty, and not as a manner of acting which we might naturally favor or which we sometime might favor. This would be tantamount to believing we could finally bring it about that, without respect for the law (which is always connected with fear or at least apprehension that we might transgress it) we, like the independent deity, might come into possession of holiness of will through irrefragable agreement of the will with the pure moral law becoming, as it were, our very nature. This pure

---

[16]To put this into more Kantian terms, to behave immorally is to allow the agreeable effect of the *material* of a maxim, whose *form* fails to conform to the principle of universality, to determine one's action. Similarly, an action has moral worth only if the *form* of the maxim conforms to the principle of universality and it is the form alone and not the material that determines one's action.

[17]*Critique of Practical Reason*, 1. 1. 32.

law, if we could never be tempted to be untrue to it, would finally cease to be a command for us.

The moral law is, in fact, for the will of a perfect being a law of holiness. For the will of any finite rational being, however, it is a law of duty, of moral constraint, and of the determination of his actions through respect for the law and reverence for its duty.[18]

In a related context in the *Foundations*, Kant writes:

A perfectly good will, therefore, would be equally subject to objective laws (of the good), but it could not be conceived as constrained by them to act in accord with them, because according to its own subjective constitution, it can be determined to act only through the conception of the good. Thus, no imperatives hold for the divine will or, more generally, for a holy will. The "ought" is here out of place, for the volition of itself is necessarily in unison with the law. Therefore imperatives are only formulas expressing the relation of objective laws of volition in general to the subjective imperfection of the will of this or that rational being, e.g., the human will.[19]

It was suggested earlier that what the theist needs in order to meet Kant's objection to the theological conception of ethics is a way of construing God's goodness so as to avoid being impaled on the autonomy horn of the Euthyphro dilemma. But perhaps we can understand God's goodness in a way that is both informative *and* consistent with holding that God's nature is the ultimate moral criterion. Our problem was generated by trying to maintain that "goodness" is a matter of fulfilling theologically grounded duties. This tells us something about the character of a finite rational creature, but in the case of God's own character it is uninformative. Thus, if we are to preserve divine goodness and avoid impalement, *His goodness must be understood in some way other than His fulfilling theologically grounded duties.* Is such a way open to the theist? William Alston, in a very provocative paper, has suggested it is:

---

[18]Ibid., 1. 1. 82-83.
[19]*Foundations*, 2. 414-15.

In the most general terms it is clear what the divine command theorist's strategy should be. He must fence in the area constituted by divine commands so that the divine nature and activity fall outside that area. This will leave him free to construe divine moral goodness in some other way.[20]

In fact, as Professor Alston has pointed out, Kant himself seems to have provided the theist with just such a route. Leaving aside the details of Kant's reasoning, it is obvious that Kant is committed to a view in which divine "goodness" must be understood in a way that excludes the notion of the fulfillment of duty. For if God is necessarily *good*, and it is the case that, for God, there are no duties, then God's goodness must consist in something other than the fulfillment of duty. But Kant obviously does *not* mean to hold a voluntaristic view in which God's "goodness" is not even remotely similar to the goodness of agents whose goodness consists in their fulfillment of moral duties. For example, he writes of the holy will that it is elevated "not indeed above all practical laws but above all practically restrictive laws, and thus above obligation and duty."[21] Were we to say that the holy will is *above* all practical laws, we would thereby commit ourselves to voluntarism. And were we to say that the holy will is *not* above all practically *restrictive* laws, we would then have to say that the goodness of that will consists in its fulfilling certain moral duties or obligations. But Kant's position might be described by saying that God's goodness consists in His being in perfect accordance with duty, but not thereby constrained by duty. Armed with this distinction, the theist is well on his way to developing an account of divine goodness that avoids being caught up in Kant's flagrant circle.

Is it plausible to think that essential perfection is incompatible with God's having moral duties? Can we agree with Kant that the "ought" is here out of place? I think that this is quite plausible. In fact, a common objection to the essential perfection view is that if God is necessarily good, then He cannot be *morally* good. Thus, Stephen Davis writes:

---

[20]William P. Alston, "What Euthyphro Should Have Said," p. 3. An early version of this paper was presented at the Pacific Regional Meeting of the Society of Christian Philosophers and has since been revised. I want to thank Professor Alston for graciously sharing a copy of the revised version with me at my request.

[21]*Critique of Practical Reason*, 1. 1. 33.

If God is actually unable to do evil it is no more morally apt to praise him for his goodness than it is apt to praise the refrigerator for keeping the food cold or a spider to refrain from telling lies. Refrigerators are designed to keep food cold; they aren't agents who make choices; it isn't praiseworthy that they keep food cold. Spiders just aren't able to tell lies; it isn't praiseworthy that they don't. If God's nature causes or determines him to do good in such a way that doing evil is not in his power, I would conclude that he is not a free and responsible moral agent and thus not a fit object of the praise and thanks of his people.[22]

This much of Davis's objection seems right. If, for example, God is so constituted that it is impossible for God to lie, then He is no more deserving of *moral* praise for refraining from lying than is the synthesized voice in my car worthy of moral praise for refraining from using four-letter expletives in reminding me to buckle up.

Given Kant's distinction it becomes clear that the goodness of God consists in something different from the goodness of finite rational creatures. To be precise, a rational creature is good to the degree that that creature fulfills his moral obligations. And, given the divine nature view, those moral obligations are constituted by the divine nature. But God *has* no moral obligations to be met. Then in what sense can God be understood to be "good"?

---

[22]Davis, *Logic and the Nature of God*, p. 95. I think that this objection to essential perfection is misguided on two counts. (1) From the view that God does not have significant *moral* freedom, it does not at all follow that He has no freedom at all. An Anselmian theist need not also be a Leibnizian theist and hold that there is only one possible world open to God. On this point, see Thomas Flint, "The Problem of Divine Freedom," *American Philosophical Quarterly* 20 (1983). See also Robert Adams, "Must God Create the Best?" *Philosophical Review* 81 (1972):317-32. (2) It is not clear that the appropriate model for the praise of God is *moral* praise. For example, as Thomas Morris has pointed out, the proper understanding of praise is an expression of gratitude to God for deigning to create in the first place, for including *me* in the creation, and for showing mercy rather than justly executing His wrath upon me as a sinner. Other models for worship seem available, which exclude the notion of moral praise. One might think the combined elements of awe and attraction in Otto's numinous experience are appropriate elements of the worship of God. Perhaps Kant's own notion of reverence for the law may even serve as a model for an appropriate expression of worship.

Thomas Morris, in seeking to reconcile essential perfection, libertarianism, and the "duty model" for divine goodness[23] has provided the resources for what I find to be an attractive solution to the Euthyphro problem. Exploiting the Kantian distinction between acting in accordance with duty and acting from duty, Morris points out that God necessarily acts in accordance with duty, but, given the fact that God is not subject to any duties, he never acts *from* duty. Thus, strictly speaking, God is not *morally* good at all. Kant's own theory commits him to the view that God's actions, as the actions of a perfectly rational being, have no moral worth, because they are akin to actions that are wholly in accord with duty, but done solely from inclination.[24] The theory I am offering accepts this implication. God's goodness, then, is understood not literally but *analogically*. God is "good" in the sense that He necessarily acts in a way that a perfectly moral agent would act, but, unlike finite moral agents, His goodness is not a matter of fulfilling moral duties. On this view, then, the literal sense of the statement "God is good" is descriptive rather than evaluative. The moral laws in accordance with which God acts, are not *prescribed* to Him, but are actually features of God's own nature, in which they have their origin.

Let us pause a moment to consider how all of this is supposed to have helped the divine nature moralist. Our problem arose in the fact that we were faced with a dilemma: either the statement "God is good" means no more than "God acts in accordance with God's nature"—which is less than newsworthy, or our understanding of divine goodness is derived from concepts not native to our original concept of God. What we needed, then, was some way of construing divine goodness which would provide it with the needed content without, at the same time, backing us onto the autonomy horn of the Euthyphro dilemma. It seems that this view allows us to ascribe "goodness" to God while, at the same time, holding that it is ultimately derived from Him. Ironically, there is a sense in which saying "God is 'good'" will turn out to mean "God acts in accordance with God's nature." But, given the view under consideration, this is not vacuous because we are informed that God's nature is itself the source of moral obligation, and so we are assured that God necessarily acts in accordance with the moral laws which we recognize. And we have avoided the autonomy horn of the dilemma

---

[23]Thomas Morris, "Duty and Divine Goodness," in *Anselmian Explorations* (Notre Dame: University of Notre Dame Press, 1987).

[24]*Foundations* 1. 398.

precisely because God's goodness is understood analogically rather than literally, so that "God is good" is a descriptive rather than an evaluative statement and, thus, does not presuppose an independent moral concept.

But several objections present themselves at this point. One of these is what we might call the *epistemological objection*. Suppose it is pointed out to the theist that many people, who have never even entertained the possibility that the nature of God is the source of moral obligation, can, in spite of that fact, recognize sound moral principles when they see them. For example, Kant's principle of humanity which affirms the intrinsic value of persons may be recognized apart from any theological considerations. In this vein, A. C. Ewing writes:

> We surely do not need any theological premiss or any special revelation from God to see that certain things such as cruelty are bad and others good. If certain acts are right and certain things are good in their intrinsic nature . . . . as we surely see they are, even God could not make them bad or wrong by willing to do so any more than he could make 2+2=5.[25]

And if, in addition to this observation, it is pointed out that we recognize that God is good, whether literally or analogically, *because of* His adherence to this principle, then seemingly we have access to this principle logically prior to any consideration of the nature of God. Are we not just in the situation that Kant pointed out, in which the affirmation of the goodness of God presupposes our own moral concepts?

But this is not our situation at all. I think the divine nature moralist has the resources for a plausible response to such a challenge. In order to appreciate his response, we must be reminded of the fact that the problem of the Euthyphro is presented as a challenge to the *internal consistency* of the theist's position. This being the case, he is entitled to appeal to elements within his theory to show his position to be coherent. One such element is the theistic doctrine of the *imago dei*. It seems plausible for the theist to account for the fact that we recognize certain moral principles—principles which are themselves expressions of relevant features of God's nature—by the fact that human beings are created in God's image. Thus, as Paul attests in the letter to the

---

[25] A.C. Ewing, "Ethics and Belief in God," *Hibbert Journal* 39 (1940-41):376.

Romans, the moral law is "inscribed upon the hearts of men."[26] It is in this same context that William Alston remarks that the theist "is free to recognize that God has so constructed us and our environment that we are led to form sound value judgments under various circumstances without tracing them back to the ultimate standard."[27] An analogous point was once made by Leibniz. On his view, the realm of the eternal verities was dependent upon the divine mind. He remarked:

> It is true that an atheist may be a geometrician: but if there were no God, geometry would have no object. And without God, not only would there be nothing existent, but there would be nothing possible. That, however, does not hinder those who do not see the necessary connection of all things one with another and with God from being able to understand certain sciences, without knowing their first source, which is in God.[28]

It seems to me, then, that it is open to the divine nature moralist to claim that God's own nature is itself the source of the moral principles by which finite rational beings are bound. The contribution of analogical predication concerning divine goodness is precisely in this fact, that it allows us to speak of God's goodness without either presupposing some independent moral principle that constitutes God's duties, or emptying the concept of divine goodness of all meaningful content. Thus, goodness is defined by reference to the nature of God, but there is no fear that, as C. S. Lewis put it, "our 'black' may be his 'white.'"

But there are further objections. If we claim that the "goodness" of God is merely descriptive of His nature, and that His nature is the source of moral obligation, and add that, in addition, God Himself is ultimately responsible for our own moral categories, then how have we said anything significantly different from Ockham's voluntarism? People have often mused that if everything in the universe were to expand proportionately, no one would ever know it because there would be nothing by which

---

[26]Romans 1.2.

[27]Alston, "What Euthyphro Should Have Said," p. 20.

[28]G.W. Leibniz, *Theodicy*, trans. by E.M. Huggard (LaSalle, IL: Open Court, 1985), p. 243. Of course the divine nature moralist, in saying that moral principles are ultimately grounded in the nature of God, is not thereby committed to Leibniz's view of the relation between God and necessary truths in general.

to measure the expansion. Thus, I could actually be millions of times larger now than I was, say, one year ago, but provided that everything else has grown in the same proportions, I would have no way of knowing it. I can imagine an objector saying that an analogous situation is possible given the divine nature theory which is here presented. For imagine a world—call it *Ock* (short for "Ockham")—in which God were to have a nature that is the moral opposite of what He has in the actual world. God's nature would be the source of moral obligation, such that one's duty is constituted by certain relevant features of that nature. In addition, human beings in Ock would be so constituted by God as to judge God's nature to be "good" in the sense that God would necessarily act in accord with those duties which they "knew" to be good. Would not the inhabitants of Ock have everything we have in the actual world, given the divine nature model here proposed? The objection capitalizes on the fact that, in such a world, the very "tests" of God's goodness are authored by God Himself. In such a world, there is no way to get outside of the categories which have been implanted by the Creator in order to know whether they are truly informative of the nature of morality. And so it would seem to be in the actual world.

This objection overlooks a crucial feature of the divine nature theory. On Ockham's view, such a state of affairs is conceivable. Given the primacy of God's will, He could presumably will and command that we hate God, steal from one another, and commit adultery, *and* so "wire" us that we intuitively recognize these actions as meritorious and obligatory. But on the theory proposed here, God is conceived as being good with *de re* necessity. This being the case, there is no world in which God exists and has a nature that is the moral opposite of that which He has in this world. Thus, the response is just that Ock is not a possible world at all.[29] And a counterexample that appeals to a logically impossible state of affairs just simply is not a counterexample at all. One might as well argue that in a world in which the sum of the interior angles of a triangle was only 90° the denizens of that world would be so constructed as to recognize this truth, and so this would not strike them as odd in any way.

---

[29]David Werther has observed that it is unclear whether this response is available to Thomas Morris and Christopher Menzel, given their view of "theistic activism" recently espoused in an article entitled "Absolute Creation" in *Anselmian Explorations*, pp. 161-78. If it is the case that God does "create His own nature," then one wonders why God could not create a nature such that Ock is a possible world.

But perhaps there is something a bit more subtle in this objection. Perhaps the concern is that there seems to be something wrong with appealing to God's nature as the ultimate moral criterion when that nature is not itself understood to be good. After all, have I not said that, literally speaking, God is not morally good, but that His adherence to moral principles is merely a descriptive fact about His nature, and they do not prescribe duties to Him? But God's nature is merely one out of an unlimited number of facts about the contours of the world. Two concerns may arise here. (1) Are we not then guilty of trying to derive "'ought' from 'is'"? After all, we seem to be inferring normative claims from a descriptive fact. And (2) is there not something rather arbitrary in choosing this particular feature of the world as the ultimate moral criterion?

I think that the first part of this objection fails to see the nature of ultimate criteria *qua* ultimate criteria. For example, Thomas Mayberry[30] has presented an illustration which I have found to be very helpful for understanding the nature of the Euthyphro dilemma. He asks us to imagine a high quality loudspeaker that has the property of high fidelity. This loudspeaker is so accurate in reproducing the sound of live music, that other loudspeakers may be evaluated by their approximation to this loudspeaker. Thus, it serves as a *standard* for all the others. But the live music is the *ultimate criterion* for evaluating *all* the loudspeakers, including the speaker of high fidelity.

Mayberry argues that for the divine command moralist to say that God is the ultimate criterion of goodness *and* that He is "good" is like trying to say that the live band is the ultimate criterion *and* that the live band has the property of high fidelity. But obviously this property is inappropriately ascribed to the live band itself because in such a context the very notion of high fidelity implies that the object having that property faithfully reproduces the sound of something else. But what is it that the live band "faithfully reproduces"? Can we say that the live band faithfully reproduces the sound of the live band? This would be inappropriate. Such properties presuppose that the object bearing those properties is being judged by some more ultimate standard or criterion. But there *is* no more ultimate criterion than the live band itself. "Goodness" is just such a property. To evaluate some object as "good" is to evaluate that object on the basis of some criterion more ultimate than itself. The divine command moralist is thus faced with a choice. On the one hand, he can understand God to be a *standard* of

---

[30]Thomas Mayberry, "Standards and Criteria: Can God Be the Standard of the Good?" *Mind* 81 (1972).

goodness in the way that the loudspeaker is the standard for all inferior speakers. In this case he is entitled to say that God is good, just as one can say that the loudspeaker has high fidelity. But if he does so choose to attribute goodness to God, he is not entitled to say that God is the ultimate criterion. It must merely be the case that God does a good job of *representing* to us whatever the ultimate criterion is. On the other hand, suppose he wants to claim that God is the ultimate moral criterion. In this case, there is, of course, no criterion more ultimate than God Himself by which God may be judged to be good, and so "goodness" is inappropriately predicated of God.

I think Mayberry is correct in his observation that the divine command moralist cannot have it both ways. God cannot be *both* the ultimate moral criterion and be understood to be morally good. But this is precisely the motivation for understanding God's goodness *analogically* rather than literally. As it turns out, Mayberry's observation becomes useful to the divine nature moralist because he has pointed out a feature of ultimate criteria in general. If God Himself is taken as the ultimate criterion, then the fact that we cannot evaluate Him as *literally* morally good is not a problem peculiar to divine nature morality. It is just a fact about *any* ultimate criterion of *any* system. Thus, it would just be wrongheaded to insist that before God can be accepted as the ultimate criterion, He be understood to be (literally) morally good Himself. It is with precisely this point in mind that Patterson Brown writes in reply to Flew and Campbell:

It surely cannot be the case that moral criteria must invariably be acquired in the context of a prior system of evaluation, or else every moral agent would have to be involved in an infinite regress of actually accepted moral standards. Since this consequence is patent nonsense, it follows that the very possibility of morality depends upon the possibility of having an ethical criterion which was not adopted by passing a moral judgment on it . . . . Campbell's contention would therefore have to be that acquiring God's will as a moral standard is essentially different from acquiring e.g., a utilitarian standard, in that the latter can be accomplished without presupposing a prior morality, whereas the former cannot. I myself can see no reason for holding this.[31]

Thus, the fact that if God is the ultimate moral criterion He must be accepted as such without having been subjected to moral evaluation is not a problem peculiar to either the divine command or the divine nature moralist. Given any ethical theory, either there is some absolute starting point for evaluation, or we have an infinite regress of moral evaluations, in which case, there just *is not* any ultimate criterion of morality, and thus nothing can ever be evaluated morally.

It is important to note that if this attempt at passing through the horns of the Euthyphro dilemma is successful, it can hardly be construed as an *ad hoc* attempt to rescue divine command morality. The key to the solution lies in the fact that God's goodness is analogical rather than literal. But this is not contrived for the sake of solving the problem of the Euthyphro. The traditional theist has wanted to hold both that God is necessarily good *and* that God is the ultimate moral criterion. Our solution of analogical goodness is a direct implication of each of these. Each is sufficient to yield the implication that divine goodness must be understood analogically.

But a final question has to do with why we should accept the view that *God* is that ultimate criterion. If there is no moral quality about God that makes Him stand out above all other proposed moral criteria, what reason is there for holding that God's nature is the correct criterion? A sufficient answer to this question would take us beyond the purpose of this essay. I have set out here only to defend the *internal coherence* of divine nature morality, and not to establish it as the true theory of morality. I do, however, think that it is arguable that God, if He exists, is as good a candidate as can be offered for the position of ultimate moral criterion. After all, if God is the source of all of creation and we hold the Anselmian view of maximal perfection, then, given the internal coherence of a divine nature morality, it seems plausible to suppose that God is also the source of morality.

But I think the most promising connection between God and morality is something along the lines of that offered by Stuart Hackett. Professor Hackett argues that only a

---

[31]Patterson Brown, "Religious Morality," in Idziak, *Divine Command Morality*, p. 257. See also Edward Wierenga, "Utilitarianism and Divine Command Theory," *American Philosophical Quarterly* 21 (1984):311-16; Alan Gewirth, *Reason and Morality* (Chicago: University of Chicago Press, 1978), pp. 12-16.

theistic world view can provide a metaphysical grounding for the notion of the intrinsic value of human beings. If he is right in this, then far from reducing our motivation to act in accordance with duty to the principle of self-love, theism would provide a strong reason for recognizing the dignity and worth of all of humanity. And this sort of connection would be in agreement with our response to the "epistemological" problem of divine nature morality to the effect that, apart from any theological considerations, people know that it is wrong to mistreat other people. Our response was simply that, given a theistic world view that holds that people are created in God's image, then this sort of thing should not be surprising. But this issue would take us far beyond our present subject, and so I refer the reader to Professor Hackett's arguments.[32]

---

[32]Stuart C. Hackett, *The Reconstruction of the Christian Revelation Claim* (Grand Rapids, MI: Baker Book House, 1982), pp. 230-42.

The Metaphysics Of Defining Death

H. M. Ducharme

University of Akron

INTRODUCTION: SUBSTANCE DUALISM
AND CHRISTIAN THEISM

Christian theism has, as indeed all religions and irreligions have, a deep-vested interest in issues concerned with truth claims about the nature of persons. In particular, does being a person necessarily require having a body? If one answers in the affirmative, then God must have a body (as is argued by numerous contemporary theists) and our own bodily death and disintegration must be our annihilation. Alternatively, if one denies that being a person requires having a functioning body, then every functioning human body need not necessarily be associated with a person—possible candidates for such states of affairs would include artificially maintained, "brain-dead" patients, anencephalic newborns, and frozen human embryos which have not yet developed a human body. Is it mind or matter that is made in the "image of God," that bears intrinsic moral value, that has the power of moral discernment? The fundamental issue requiring resolution here is whether a person is essentially an immaterial substance (a mind or a soul), or whether a material body is necessarily required for a person to exist. It is the metaphysical debate between substance (mind-body) dualism and materialism. The traditional position entailed in and advanced by Christian theism is clearly identifiable as substance dualism. A man living on Earth consists of two substances, a body and a soul, a material substance and an immaterial substance. And although the two substances have a unique interaction, a person is essentially a separable mind or soul. Thus it is that St. Paul can be clearly understood to prefer "to be away from the body and at home with the Lord" (2 Cor. 5:8); St. Augustine unambiguously argues that "the mind knows itself, it knows its own substance" (*Trinity*, 10.10.16) and "that the soul comes from God" which God made "immortal in His own likeness" (*The Magnitude of the Soul*, Ch. 2); and Calvin asserts that dualism of soul and body "ought to be beyond controversy" because "from Scripture" we are "taught that the soul is an incorporeal substance . . . something separate from God" (*Institutes* I:184, 185, 192), whose chief activity it is to aspire to union with God. (See also John Calvin, *An excellent treatise of the Immortalytie of the soule, by which is proved, that the soules, after their departure out of the bodies, are awake and doe lyve, contrary to that erronious opinion of certain ignorant persons, who thinke them to lye a sleape untill the day of Judgement,* translated from the French by T. Stocker, 1581.) Thus it is historically true that dualism is the traditional view of Christian theism, but it is one traditional view that is no longer the dominant view of man held by contemporary theists. The dominant contemporary view among theologians (liberal, moderate, and conservative) is the so-called holistic or psychosomatic unity view. In philosophical terms these are variants of substance monism or materialism, either reductive materialism, non-reductive materialism, dual-property or dual-aspect materialism. Prior to the past half-century, these faces of materialism—whether traced to Empedocles, or Hobbes, or Feuerbach, or Marx—were seen as heretical to the faith. Today, the psychosomatic unity view is the dominant fashion among theologians, and dualism is shunned as a perverse Greek infiltration.

In this article, the traditional, non-fashionable view of mind-body dualism is defended and applied to the contemporary debate concerning the redefinition of death.

THE METAPHYSICS OF DEFINING DEATH

Is it the case that any definition of the death of an individual is a metaphysical issue? With respect to this question, three major traditions of contemporary philosophy—empiricism, existentialism/phenomenology, and contemporary philosophical theology—seem to agree. They agree by rejecting a realist metaphysics, if not an outright rejection of metaphysics altogether. This *a priori* rejection includes metaphysical concepts of persons which logically imply a non-realist or anti-realist definition of death. This is an unfortunate meeting place of philosophical traditions because, if I am not mistaken, these groups have lost their way.[1] The task of this paper is to show, by way of example, that the President's Commission's statute in *Defining Death,* which claims to be metaphysically neutral, is in fact a metaphysical definition, one which is metaphysically partisan and biased favoring non-realism and anti-realism. Because of this bias its implications for public policy require scrutiny, a scrutiny only briefly begun in this paper.

Basic Argument

1. Any definition of death of an individual presupposes and entails some particular (metaphysical) concept of persons.

2. The President's Commission claims to identify the necessary and sufficient conditions for the death of an individual from a theory-neutral, non-metaphysical vantage point; from "the scientific viewpoint."[2]

3. It follows that the President's Commission's claim is false.

What is meant in proposition (1), concerning the presupposition and entailment of a concept of persons, can be explained by way of example. Consider the following lists of epistemically innocent propositions about individuals.[3]

---

[1]Cf. Roderick M. Chisholm, *Person and Object* (London: George Allen & Unwin, 1976), p. 23.

[2]President's Commission for the Study of Ethical Problems in Medicine and Biomedical and Behavioral Research, *Defining Death* (Washington, DC: U.S. Government Printing Office, 1981), p. 31.

[3]These lists are adapted from Chisholm, *Person and Object*, pp. 15-18.

List I

1. I am now thinking such-and-such things, that is, certain beliefs, desires, or attitudes.

2. I now have a body of such-and-such size.

3. I am now intentionally bringing about such-and-such things I could have avoided bringing about.

This list of propositions in the present tense can be as easily affirmed when changed to the past tense.

List II

4. In 1970 I had such-and-such thoughts.

5. In 1970 I had a body of such-and-such size.

6. In 1970 I intentionally brought about such-and-such things which I could have avoided bringing about.

Thus, as the schematic list is applicable to any individual (as one applies it by filling in details about himself), we can see that we all do presuppose and assume in our ordinary activities a particular concept of ourselves as an individual or person. The various items in the two lists pertain to *one and the same entity* throughout. An individual, or person, is that which *endures* through the variables, is non-identical with the variable (in part or in whole), and is that which *unites* the variables, an *ens per se*. Thus a person is an immaterial substance who is very much in touch with material things.

There will, of course, be philosophical objections quickly forthcoming against substance dualism. My general reply is two-fold. (1) Whatever we are justified in assuming when we are not doing philosophy, we are also justified in assuming when we *are* doing philosophy, at least until we have positive reasons for thinking these assumptions to be false. (2) The lists show all that is required for my argument, namely, that a concept of persons *is* assumed and entailed in even such simple propositions about individuals.

There may be two initial objections to the second premise of my argument. (1) It may be objected that the Commission gives only necessary but not necessary and sufficient conditions for the definition of death. This objection is easily shown to be erroneous by reference to the Commission's report itself; for example, their explicit rejection of cessation of upper brain function as a sufficient condition:

> The President's Commission, as subsequent chapters explain more fully, *regards* the cessation of the vital functions of the entire brain—*and not merely* portions thereof, such as those responsible for cognitive functions—*as the only proper* neurological basis for declaring death.[4]

(2) The second objection, closely associated with the first, is that the Commission does not offer a definition of the death of *persons* (which would unmistakably be a metaphysical issue) but offers merely a "consensus," a physiological definition of "brain death." My reply to this objection is both "yes" and "no." "Yes," the Commission does claim to be offering a physiological definition of death: ". . . the 'definition' contained in the statute ought to address general *physiological standards* rather than medical criteria and tests . . ." (p. 1; emphasis added in this and the immediately following quotations). But "no," the Commission *in fact* stipulates a definition of death of persons. My point here can be clarified if it is asked of the Commission: "the definition of death *of what?*" On my reading of the report I find no less than eleven varied answers: for example, that they are defining "the death of a *human being*" (p. 3 and p. 7); alternatively, "the Commission's mandate is . . . to provide clear and principled guidance for determining whether such [artificially-maintained] *bodies* are alive or dead" (p. 3); also, "extending the 'definition' of death beyond those lacking *all* brain functions to include, for example, *persons* who have lost only cognitive functions but are still able to breathe spontaneously would radically change the *meaning* of death" (p. 7); and when "the traditional signs of life—respiration and

---

[4]President's Commission, *Defining Death*, p. 18, emphasis added.

heartbeat—disappear: the *person* is dead" (p. 15); about patients with only brain stem function—"such *persons* may exhibit spontaneously, involuntary movements such as yawns or facial grimaces, their eyes may be open and they may be capable of breathing without assistance" (p. 18); death has occurred "when *a patient* has *become a dead body*" (p. 24); and the Commission concludes, in harmony with physicians who were previously applying heart/lung criteria that, "They were affirming only that the loss of those functions indicated *that a person had died*" (p. 56). Thus, this evidence from the report itself clearly reveals that a concept of persons is presupposed by the Commission and that in fact it is defining the death of persons and/or human beings. The following, more particular, argument begins with the statue itself, which stipulates when "*an individual . . . is dead*." Thus, unless (and even if) we are to understand "an individual" to be a functioning brain, the statute itself is clearly not theory-free but theory-laden concerning the nature and concept of persons.

PARTICULAR CRITICISM OF THE PRESIDENT'S COMMISSION

The President's Commission worked with the American Bar Association, the American Medical Association, and the National Conference of Commissioners on Uniform State Laws in formulating the Uniform Determination of Death Act (which is now enshrined in the laws of more than 40 states). It stipulates that:

An individual who has sustained either (1) irreversible cessation of circulatory and respiratory functions, or (2) irreversible cessation of all functions of the entire brain, including the brain stem, is dead. A determination of death must be made in accordance with accepted medical standards.[5]

This definition clearly resolves the case where no brain activity is present but heart and lungs continue to be "artificially" maintained by the use of a respirator. It offers an unobjectionable, sufficient condition for the determination of death. But the Commission stipulates both the necessary and sufficient conditions for the

---

[5]Ibid., p. 2.

determination of death,[6] and in so doing it presupposes a reductive materialist's concept of persons. This can be seen in its four arguments against the "higher-brain" formulations, which it calls "personhood" arguments.

The No Band-Wagon Argument

The Commission argues that "crucial to the personhood argument is acceptance of one particular concept of those things that are essential to being a person, while there is no general agreement on this very fundamental point among philosophers, much less physicians or the general public."[7] The inference drawn is that because there is no consensus among philosophers, physicians, or the general public about what constitutes a person, such arguments are positively unhelpful and actually misguided.

Such an argument is an instance of a "no band-wagon" fallacy. Why this type of argument is invalid can be readily illustrated from pre-Civil War America: "Since there is no consensus that Negroes are persons, it is not correct to believe anyone who says that they are." Certainly popular acceptance of a policy does not prove it to be true and/or right, and absence of general assent to a claim does not prove it to be false. It is illogical and deceptive to conclude from the premise "There exists no consensus on a definition of death," that "The whole brain oriented definition should be chosen."[8]

The Commission may have been meaning to argue that since there is no consensus, society should take the safer course and opt for the whole brain oriented concept of death so that no one may be treated as dead who could by some philosophical views be alive. If that is the Commission's position, however, it is an argument in favor of adopting a heart and lung oriented concept of death, or the cessation of the flow of bodily fluids criterion, the view held by some Orthodox Jews and American Indians.

---

[6]See C. Pallis, "Whole-brain death reconsidered—physiological facts and philosophy," *Journal of Medical Ethics* 9 (1983):32-37.

[7]President's Commission, *Defining Death*, p. 39.

[8]Robert M. Veatch, "Whole Brain and Higher Brain Related Concepts of Death: A Critique of the President's Commission" in *"Whole Brain and Higher Brain Related Concepts of Death: A Critique of the President's Commission,"* ed. Richard Zahner (Dordrecht: D. Reidel, forthcoming). I am indebted to Veatch's essay for the identification of various arguments entailed in the Commission's *Defining Death*.

Begging the Question and the Breathing Body Argument

A second argument offered by the Commission against arguments derived from concepts of personal identity is equally fallacious. The Commission argues that:

> The implication of the personhood and personal identity arguments is that Karen Quinlan, who retains brain stem function and breathes spontaneously, is just as dead as a corpse in the traditional sense. The Commission rejects this conclusion and the further implication that such patients could be buried or otherwise treated as dead persons.[9]

Disregarding the claim that all arguments from personal identity deliver the same (unacceptable) answer about Karen Quinlan type cases, another problem follows on the heels of this hasty generalization, namely, the implication that is said to follow from personal identity arguments. The claim is that personal identity arguments conclude that Karen Quinlan (assuming only brain stem function—which was, in fact, not the case) "is just as dead as a corpse." Evidently the Commission expects this "just as" to function as a *reductio ad absurdum* against arguments that begin with the concept of what a person is. In fact, their supposed *reductio* fallaciously begs the question at issue. Does the proper name "Karen Quinlan" refer to a person or not? They silently assume the proposition that the name does refer to the person of Karen Quinlan, yet claim that their *reductio* demonstrates that personhood arguments are unbelievable. Hence their argument is, at best, incapable of establishing the truth of its conclusion and, at worst, self-contradictory because it employs a concept of personal identity to argue that personal identity arguments are absurd.

A final problem with this argument is the "further implication" that the Commission holds to follow from personal identity arguments, namely, that those who propose a neocortical criterion of death would bury a body even while it continued to breathe and have a heart beat. This implication, however, does not necessarily follow from the neocortical criterion, and in fact no proponent of it (that I am aware of) would draw this implication. For example, Robert Veatch writes that "On aesthetic grounds I would want to disconnect the respirator and let his heart stop before burial." But even if it is

---

[9]President's Commission, *Defining Death*, p. 40.

aesthetically offensive to bury a breathing body, an aesthetic reason for action is different in kind than a moral reason for action. One is not obligated to act in accord with aesthetics. One is, however, obligated to act in accord with morality. The question then is, are there any good moral reasons for not burying breathing bodies? It seems to me that there are. (1) Simply because a person is not present is no reason to disrespect a person's property. It is *prima facie* wrong to haul Paul's car off to the junk yard just because he is not in it; it is *prima facie* wrong to cart Paul's body off to the cemetery just because he is no longer associated with it. We have direct moral responsibilities to persons and their property, and there is no more personal, private property that any person has than his body. (2) We ought to respect a person's legal will and his "living will." So ought we to respect stipulations which the President's Commission may need to have spelled out in one's living will, for example, "after my death please disconnect any artificial supports and allow my body's functions to expire before proceeding with removal to the morgue." Common sense and simple respect for the dead would normally seem to be instructive about such details. (3) It is *prima facie* wrong to bury breathing bodies just as it is *prima facie* wrong to drop non-breathing bodies from fourth floor ICU windows. Thus the breathing body argument is not a sound argument against a higher-brain criterion of death.

The Lack of Adequate Technology Argument

The Commission also rejects the personal identity/higher-brain criterion of death because there are at present no techniques available in neurophysiology sufficient to translate it into public policy.[10] This is a very important concern, but it is nonetheless a misplaced argument. It is a misplaced argument because it does not follow from the fact that there are no techniques available to distinguish higher-brain function from brain stem function, that the higher-brain function is incorrect and that the whole-brain criterion is correct. Just because technological expertise is not sufficiently advanced to locate and measure higher-brain functions does not count against the position that persons ought to be considered dead when it *can* be determined that they have irreversibly lost higher-brain function.[11] In fact, it is actually refreshing to have a

---

[10]Ibid., p. 40.

[11]This argument is in Veatch, "Critique," forthcoming.

philosophical refinement already on the board *prior to* technological advances. It is also worth noting that such advances are not far off. It is now possible, using three-dimensional positron emission tomography, to obtain a secure finding of neocortical death in spite of residual brain stem function.[12] In terms of policy considerations, even if PET scanning *is* inadequate, employing the whole-brain criterion does not count against the position that says humans ought to be treated as dead once the loss of higher-brain function has been established. It only shows that when in doubt one ought to favor life.

The New Criterion Entails a New Concept of Death Argument

The final argument given by the Commission against the higher-brain criterion is the claim that "the adoption of a higher-brain 'definition' would depart radically from the traditional standards,"[13] and "greater consensus than now [must] exist before taking the major step of radically revising the concept of death."

Such a claim is controversial on several counts even if we overlook its "band-wagon" fallacy. First, this claim blends and confuses the concept of death and the criterion of death. No progress will be made in this discussion if such a basic distinction is abused. The Commission assumes the truth of two hidden premises: (1) that the whole-brain *criterion* of death is the traditional *concept* of death, and (2) that there is one "traditional" concept of death, *and* this is the one entailed in the Commission's total-brain definition of death.

The first hidden premise is simply false. As noted above, the concept of death is non-identical with the criterion of death. The second hidden premise is also false, but a more extensive discussion is required to show this to be the case.

Two items require clarification here. The first is that the concept of death necessarily presupposes the concept of a person, for it is the death of a person that is of central concern. Death is an event but death is not a substance, agent, or ontological entity. Death is an event that obtains in the personal history of a human being. Thus

---

[12]See Roland Puccetti, "Neocortical Definitions of Death and Philosophical Concepts of Persons," in *Whole Brain and Higher Brain Related Concepts of Death: A Critique of the President's Commission,* ed. Richard Zahner (Dordrecht: D. Reidel, forthcoming).

[13]President's Commission, *Defining Death,* p. 40.

talk of the "concept of death" is a dangling, parasitic concept because it is the concept of the death of a person of which we seek an adequate definition. Those views which deny this *prima facie* claim bear the burden of proof.

The second clarification is concerned with what constituents the Commission intends to mark out by use of the term "traditional" concept. It appears the term "traditional" is taken to cover the position philosophers term the "common" view, the "common-sense view," or the realist's view. If this is correct, then significant headway can be made, namely, the common-sense concept of a person will be determinative of the common-sense concept of the death of a person. On the former there is broad agreement. The common-sense understanding of the nature of man is said to be embedded in ordinary language, and is identified as substance dualism (person-body or mind-body dualism). Even though substance dualism is unfashionable in certain academic and theological circles at present, there is a broad consensus even among its opponents (materialists)—Thomas Hobbes, Daniel Dennett, David Lewis, Thomas Nagel, Brian O'Shaughnessy, Richard Rorty, J. J. C. Smart and Derek Parfit, for example—that dualism is the common-sense (or realist) view of man.[14]

---

[14]Thomas Hobbes, *The English Works of Thomas Hobbes of Malmesbury* (London: John Bohn, 1839), IV: 62; Daniel Dennett, *Content and Consciousness* (London: Routledge & Kegan Paul, 1969), pp. 3-5; David Lewis, "An Argument for the Identity Theory," *Journal of Philosophy* 63 (1966):25; Thomas Nagel, "Physicalism," *Philosophical Review* 74 (1965):340; Brian O'Shaughnessy, *The Will*, 2 vols. (Cambridge: Cambridge University Press, 1980), I:29; Richard Rorty, *Philosophy and the Mirror of Nature* (Oxford: Basil Blackwell, 1980), p. 17; J.J.C. Smart, "Materialism," *Journal of Philosophy* 60 (1963):661; and Derek Parfit, *Reasons and Persons* (Oxford: Oxford University Press, 1984), pp. ix-x, 219. It is important to note here that the traditional Christian view of the death of a human person is an event wherein the soul (which is the self or person) leaves the body to be with its Maker. It is a theological doctrine that *prima facie* entails substance dualism. St. Augustine: ". . . the soul . . . (is) itself neither a body nor in any way like a body" (*The Magnitude of the Soul*, Ch. 13). The soul is the mind, such that St. Augustine is his mind (or soul) who has a body: "I am the one who is remembering, I am the mind" (*Confessions*, Bk. 10, Chap. 16). St. Thomas Aquinas: ". . . the intellective soul by which man understands and which transcends the condition of corporeal matter, must not be wholly encompassed by or imbedded in matter, as material forms are" (*Summa contra gentiles* 2.68.12 and *Summa theologiae* 1.75.2). Souls can and do exist independently of the body (but not perpetually so): "Since, then, it [the soul, or self] persists perpetually, it must once again be united to the body; and this is to rise again. Therefore, the immortality of souls seems to demand a future resurrection of bodies (*Summa contra*

Employing these two clarifications, the appropriate common-sense concept of *death* will be that death *is the passing away of the person*, that is, the passing away of a being essentially characterized as a rational, sentient, moral agent. (Whether or not the person continues to exist after death is a separate issue; one which ought not to be entailed in legislative definitions.) The *criterion* of death is third person evidence that may or may not justify an inference as to whether or not the person in question has passed away. More precisely, given substance dualism and assuming two-way interactionism, irreversible loss of higher-brain function is sufficient evidence to justify the inference that the possibility of interaction has been destroyed and that the person has passed away. In contrast with substance dualism, a mind/brain identity theorist will hold that the criterion of the cessation of brain activity is the *ceasing to be of a person* because a person is a functioning body. (Such a view is not neutral about the possibility of personal existence after bodily death and thus entails an anti-theological implication, one contrary to traditional Judeo-Christian beliefs.) It is just such a *revisionist* concept of persons and death that is held by Green and Wikler.

The point of showing that the concept and criterion of death are separate, distinct issues for the "traditional," common-sense dualist, but basically the same issue for the non-traditional, mind/brain identity theorist can now be made explicit. The point is that the Commission's claim that the "traditional" concept of death entails a total-brain criterion of death is false, on either of two interpretations. On the one hand, if the Commission intentionally conflates the concept of death into a criterion of death, then they are presupposing a materialist concept of human persons. If this is their intention, then their claim is false because the "traditional" concept of persons is substance dualism and not materialism. On the other hand, if the Commission intends to unpack a truth about the "traditional" concept, then they are also wrong, for the traditional concept of persons implies a higher-brain, not a total-brain, criterion of death. The

---

gentiles 4.82.10). For John Calvin's view see his treatise on the immortality of the soul cited in the text.

Veatch sympathetically cites William May concerning the traditional Judeo-Christian view, who writes: "A man not only *has* a body, he *is* his body . . ." (William May, "Attitudes toward the Newly Dead," *Hastings Center Studies* 1 [1973]; 3, cited in Robert Veatch, *Death, Dying and the Biological Revolution* [New Haven: Yale University Press], pp. 253-254). According to Augustine, Aquinas, and Calvin, May's position is contradictory to the traditional Christian view.

Commission mixes apples and oranges; it cannot have it both ways. If they want to defend the total-brain criterion, they must give up the "traditional" concept of person. If they want to defend the "traditional" concept of person, they must give up the total-brain criterion.

CRITICISM OF VEATCH

In a recent paper Robert Veatch writes that the Green and Wikler argument which draws on the concept of personal identity is "one of the most sophisticated presentations that seems to support a higher-brain oriented formulation."[15] Veatch himself argues that the higher-brain formulation is correct, but it need not be employed or presupposed in order to define death. He claims to be able to define death independently of any particular concept of persons.

How does Veatch claim to accomplish this? He does it by defining death as "the name we give to the condition under which it is considered appropriate to initiate a series of behaviors that are normally initiated when we call someone dead."[16]

If Veatch is correct, however, his anti-metaphysical definition of death will entail significant complications. For example, I would never die if I could so orchestrate events such that no "appropriate" sociological death behaviors followed my metaphysical demise. If I gradually withdrew from society, eventually moving to a deserted island in the Pacific, so that no one remembered me and no one knew when my heart stopped beating and my brain-wave activity ceased, I would never die. But, on the other hand, a sociological definition of death could kill me before my time. Not long ago an East Coast man snapped out of fifteen years of amnesia.[17] The onset of amnesia occurred while he was away from home. He could not remember his name, whether or not he was married, or where he lived. After seven years of absence, his wife had gone through all the "appropriate" death behaviors and even had him legally declared dead. But in 1985 he regained his memory, whereupon he returned to his old home address, knocked on the door, and greeted his wife. According to Veatch's definition of death, this man was dead (according to his wife's behavior) *and* alive

---

[15]Veatch, "Critique," forthcoming.

[16]Ibid.

[17]Evening News, CBS affiliate, Washington, D.C., December 28, 1985.

(according to those with whom he lived for fifteen years). Furthermore, even though he was literally alive, he came back from death the day he greeted his wife on the front steps. It is evident that a sociological definition of death that entails such contradictions cannot be correct. Veatch might reply here that his sociological definition is not shown to be false; rather, these particular cases are merely instances of inappropriate behavior due to inconclusive evidence. This reply, however, assumes that there is both an appropriate time and situation when death behavior is appropriate. The appropriate time would be that time *determined by the event of death*, and *not* the other way around as he would have it. Sociological behavior cannot causally determine the metaphysical death of a person. The ox comes before the cart.

CONCLUSION

In conclusion, I have argued that a concept of persons is entailed in the definition of death. Consequently, those definitions of death that claim logical independence of a concept of persons are wholly inadequate and false. I have also argued that contemporary debates on this issue have conflated the "traditional" *concept* of death into arguments about the *criterion* of death. The "traditional" (common, or realist) view of human persons is substance dualism, which entails a concept of death as an event, which most coherently implies a higher-brain criterion of death. The non-traditional (revisionary) view of human persons is materialism, which entails a concept of death as a process, which most coherently implies a total-brain criterion of death. How then should we *not* define death? We should not define death by building an argument on a tremulous foundation. We should not define the death of a person irrespective of what a person is. We should not because we cannot.

But if we cannot define death without an entailed metaphysics of persons, and since wars have been waged over different metaphysical beliefs, is it beneficial to drag this difference out into the light of public policy? It seems to me that it is highly advantageous, and in fact a consensus can even be forthcoming if some care is given to sort out one's basic metaphysical commitments. The consensus that can be delivered (as suggested below) is one that is able to go much further toward settling hostile viewpoints on public issues because it is able to respect the metaphysical theories that are precious to their proponents. The Commission's consensus is one that tries to settle the debate by unsuccessfully attempting to avoid the metaphysical issues.

There are three principal options available in defining death: (1) Favor one metaphysical concept at the expense of the others; but this would be impractical and immoral in a pluralistic society. (2) Adopt several definitions of death as legal options from which individuals may choose; but this will lead to innumerable legal and moral problems that could be avoided. (3) Adopt a consensus definition of death. If we assume that adopting a consensus definition of death, if possible, is preferable in a pluralistic society, then the issue reduces to arriving at a definition that is consistent with the broadest range of constituents and offends the fewest constituents. It has been shown above that the Uniform Determination of Death Act, in effect, is a consensus view only for some American Indians and certain Orthodox Jews. Hence the total-brain definition of death makes it illegal to act in accordance with common-sense realism, Judeo-Christian beliefs (substance dualism), and most applications of reductive and non-reductive materialism (Green/Wikler, Michael Tooley, H. Tristram Engelhardt, Jr., Karen Grandstand Gervais, for example, argue for a higher-brain criterion of death).[18]

It follows that a higher-brain criterion of death ought to be adopted in public policy. Such a proposal is not "the most radical" among the alternatives, as its opponents claim; it is the policy most consistent with common-sense realism. The current total-brain criterion of death entails a non-realist or anti-realist concept of persons, which truly *is* a radical position on which to ground a public policy. But, as a certain amount of time will be required for the general public to identify more carefully the common-sense criterion of death, given today's bio-technical advances, two implications follow: (1) it is appropriate to allow people to continue to elect a total-brain criterion, but (2) it ought not to be illegal to act now or in the future in accord with common-sense.

I wish to express my appreciation to Ray Moseley for his helpful comments in the development of this paper and also to the Department of Community Health and Family Medicine in the College of Medicine, University of Florida, for the initial financial

---

[18]See Karen Grandstand Gervais, *Redefining Death* (New Haven: Yale University Press, 1986), pp. 157-58, 215-16, for a thoroughgoing argument for a neocortical concept of persons and hence neocortical criterion of death.

support of this research. James H. Buchanan, William E. McMahon, Alan Hart, and Kathleen Dixon have given me helpful criticisms of later drafts of this paper.

But The Greatest Of These Is Desire

Glenn A. Hartz

Ohio State University at Mansfield

I am not really going to try here to refute one of St. Paul's central claims about the surpassing merit of Christian love. But I do wish to show that the desires which partly constitute love and other states of mind central to Christian living are at least as ethically important as those states of mind themselves. I shall begin by pointing out that what I call *moral desires*—for example, wanting revenge—have moral status in their own right and typically act as a main ingredient in ethically significant emotions and attitudes. The second section is an attempt to locate a suitable meta-ethical account of how such states of mind can have this status. After considering alternatives, I argue that the most adequate position is one which claims that these states of mind are virtuous just in case they are character traits manifested by or commanded by God, and not virtuous otherwise. In the third section I explore the relation between relatively low-level moral desires and those few I call "master desires"—that is, those which have among their objects the full range of lower level desires. Master desires tend to act as one's dominant controlling perspective, and I argue that steering one's states of mind in a more godly direction requires that one replace one's natural, overall selfish master desire with one directed towards pleasing God. Finally, I raise the issue concerning which rules one might follow in order to cultivate more virtuous states of mind.

MORAL DESIRES AND THEIR RELATION
TO ATTITUDES AND EMOTIONS

First I must indicate what I take moral desires to be. I wish to eliminate from the running such instinctive appetites as hunger, thirst, and sexual urges. I wish also to disqualify such "sense-desires"[1] as the want to have one's back massaged or to avoid being in the vicinity of sauerkraut. In addition I rule out such taste-desires as the desire to listen to the Beatles rather than Bach or to paint a room lavender rather than antique white. I have no fancy architectonic machinery to render this move apodeictically certain. It just seems true that those desires seldom if ever have a moral dimension. Consider that it would be quite strange under any circumstances to blame or praise someone for desiring liquids or a massage or lavender decor.

One prominent reason for this is the fact that having or not having the relevant wants is never under direct voluntary control: One does not in any sense decide whether one desires water or lavender or wants to visit the masseur. And, as Bishop Butler observes, this fact is sufficient to render the items in question morally moot:

> We never, in the moral way, applaud or blame either ourselves or others for what we enjoy or what we suffer . . . [when] we consider [that thing] as altogether out of our power, but only for what we do or would have done had it been in our power; or for what we leave undone, which we might have done or would have left undone, though we could have done it.[2]

One can, of course, starve one's desire for, say, the Turkish Tickle—possibly motivated by the fact that regularly paying for a massage of this kind interferes with

---

[1]N.J.H. Dent calls such desires "sense-desires" in Chapter 2 of *The Moral Psychology of the Virtues* (Cambridge: Cambridge University Press, 1984).

[2]Joseph Butler, "A Dissertation upon the Nature of Virtue," in *Five Sermons*, ed. Stuart M. Brown, Jr. (Indianapolis: Bobbs-Merrill, 1950), p. 83. The issue over whether lack of voluntariness is always sufficient to rule out moral blame and praise is controversial. Robert M. Adams presents a convincing case for the belief that ingratitude may be manifested or acted on involuntarily, yet nevertheless be blameworthy. See his "Involuntary Sins," *The Philosophical Review* 94 (1985):3-31.

one's economic obligations (it costs more than one's family's budget allows) or with one's moral principles (it is available only in the city's "sin district"). But this is a case of blaming one's acting to fulfill and (thereby) reinforce the desire in a particular context and society; it does not in the least prove that the desire itself is wrong. And similarly for the rest of the desires I have mentioned—none is a candidate for moral value because none is under direct voluntary control.

Of course, these desires might be under *indirect* voluntary control if they are related systematically to voluntary choices. One's desire for revenge, for instance, might be acquired and sustained indirectly through other choices. Suppose I have not willfully chosen to cultivate the desire for revenge. Nevertheless, over the past five months I *have* willfully allowed myself to cultivate a singular hatred for my loan officer. As a result, the desire to bring retribution upon Jack Becker for the disruptions his negligence has visited upon my family flourishes in my heart right along with the hate. In this case, even though the desire is not ever directly chosen, it certainly is tightly linked to my voluntarily maintained hatred.

Sensory and taste-based appetites are not like the desire for revenge in this sense: They do not come along as natural concomitant effects of our decisions. This is another reason I attribute no ethical dimension to them.

But voluntariness is not a sufficient condition for moral desirehood. I can deliberately try to develop in myself the desire to work on this paper today, yet that desire does not so far forth count as a moral desire. It will be a moral desire only if the processes which generate the choice and the desire manifest my moral character. Suppose that I have been struggling to keep from writing this paper, even though I know God wants me to write it. Today I finally obey by doing everything I can to motivate myself to write it. Given these background facts, along with the assumption that dealings of this kind with the Almighty are moral issues, it is easy to see that we have on our hands a moral desire. On the other hand, if my choosing to cultivate that desire is the result of a whimsical feeling of writer's abandon which just happens to come over me suddenly, then the desire is not a moral one. (To discern between upshots and non-upshots of moral character, it seems clear that one must employ one's ethical intuitions about what moral character involves: I have no deep argument to offer to those who disagree with my way of drawing the distinction in particular cases.)

Moral desires, then, reflect one's moral character. They reveal how the self is getting on with its distinctively ethical projects. Evil desires include wanting revenge or desiring that evil befall someone; among the good desires are wanting to encourage a sick friend or to be honest.

These points about voluntariness and manifesting one's moral character lead us to see that we can not take

1. Jones has a bad (good) desire x

to entail

2. Jones is open to blame (praise) for having x,

since it may not in any sense have been up to Jones whether he has x, or having x may not at all express his moral character. When the processes which instill x in Jones completely circumvent his direct or indirect voluntary intervention as well as his moral character, we will say that there are *sufficient excusing conditions* to disqualify him as a candidate for blame or praise for having x. Thus (2) must be changed to

2'. In the absence of sufficient excusing conditions, Jones is open to blame (praise) for having x.

But even (2') is defective as it stands. It leads us to believe that the excusing conditions we have discussed are the only ones which can block out blame or praise. This is not so: We have overlooked cases where ethical considerations garnered from the context override the blame. Suppose that Dietrich Bonhoeffer voluntarily came to possess the desire for revenge against Hitler. He realized the desire was developing, but did not do what he might have done to stifle it. Moreover, for the sake of argument, at least, let us suppose this desire reflects to a certain extent his overall moral character: He believes Christians should take into their own hands the process of bringing retribution upon the heads of those who promote violence of such magnitude. If (2') were allowed to stand, it would force us to blame Bonhoeffer in this case, since neither excusing condition is fulfilled. However, it seems he is not blameworthy because the extreme moral provocation Hitler has created justifies Bonhoeffer's desire for revenge in this case. We must qualify (2′) to specify *prima facie* blame and praise, so that (1) will be taken to entail

> 2″. If there are not sufficient excusing conditions, Jones is open to *prima facie* blame (praise) for having *x*.

Bonhoeffer's *prima facie* blame is done away by overriding moral considerations. Applying this to a case of praise, we can say that most or all of the praise which is *prima facie* due Char for desiring to take care of her aged mother is canceled when one finds that the underlying motive is to be remembered handsomely in the family will. (Of course, a problem which becomes especially troubling at this point is that of deciding how to *describe* the relevant desires. We could re-describe Bonhoeffer's desire, for example, as the desire to take revenge as a last resort on a willful and unrelenting scoundrel—and that would make his original desire seem less evil than it seemed when described more vaguely as the desire to take revenge. Similarly, Char's desire might be better described as the desire to get money from her mother's estate by helping her through old age—and this would make Char's original moral rating look much less positive.)

Evaluating the moral status of a person who has a desire thus involves considering the entire story—not simply the question whether the desire is good or evil, but also whether the person to any extent voluntarily cultivated it, whether it was cleared through his moral character, and whether there might be morally relevant conditions to override his *prima facie* blame or praise. The degree of actual blame or praise we attribute to him will vary in its strength according to the presence or absence of these conditions.

Since our central concern is with the relation between moral desires and emotions and attitudes, I shall now analyze those latter states of mind.

I take the concept of emotion to be one which performs the convenient role of rounding up several types of mental or bodily states typically found together and assigning them a certain unity. It is notoriously difficult to find a set of necessary and sufficient conditions which pick out all and only the emotions, and I am not going to try that here. Instead, I shall offer an informal analysis.[3] (In the definition of EMO below, sets are allowed to have only one member.)

EMO: An emotion is typically a combination of some or all of the factors (a)-(d):

(a) a consciously or unconsciously held[4] set of beliefs, one of which is usually an evaluation of a situation as desirable or undesirable

(b) a consciously or unconsciously held set of desires

(c) bodily sensations and/or mental feelings

(d) an upset bodily condition.

Strictly speaking, this is my analysis of an *occurrent emotional state*: It applies to cases where one is actually now flush with embarrassment or overcome by guilt or emboldened by courage. By contrast, *dispositional emotions* need not be currently going on in a person in order for him to have them. We will say that when one has a

---

[3]This analysis owes much to William P. Alston's article, "Emotion and Feeling," in *The Encyclopedia of Philosophy*, 8 vols., ed. Paul Edwards (New York: Macmillan Publishing Co. and The Free Press, 1967), 2: 479-86.

[4]For arguments in favor of allowing unconscious beliefs and desires into one's formulation of emotion-related factors, see William Lyons, *Emotion* (Cambridge; Cambridge University Press, 1980), pp. 85-89 and 167-68. In brief, he argues that if conscious beliefs and desires were insisted upon, many cases when the evaluation short-circuits consciousness would not be explainable on cognitivist assumptions. That is, we often need to attribute to someone who is in an emotional state unconscious beliefs and desires which can act as causal determinants of that state. The beliefs are given a dispositional analysis by Lyons. He says, "An evaluation can be active but not conscious" (p. 88), and he also thinks desires can be active but not conscious. I believe Lyons's handling of the cases he discusses is an adequate defense of the cognitivist position on this issue, and I shall not discuss it further here.

dispositional emotion one is such that one is frequently apt to be in a corresponding occurrent emotional state. Thus I have dispositional pride if, in situations where I earn some distinctive recognition, I am likely to become occurrently proud.

I cannot give a full-dress defense of definition EMO here. But I will say that given my preference for a *cognitive* theory of emotion, I am going to be taking conditions (a) and (b) to be the most critical ones.[5] It seems clear on reflection that (c) and (d) are mere window-dressing by comparison with (a) and (b). Consider an example: Suppose we have the occurrently proud chap here—let it be Jones. Jones has a central evaluative belief—say, that his paper's being published in *The Philosophical Review* is a most desirable thing. Having described the belief in this way, it is natural to attribute to Jones a desire to have an article published there, as well as related desires for the prestige and notariety which come along with such a publication. If he did not have these desires, it is hard to see how he might rationally have arrived at his central evaluative belief that getting the publication is *desirable*. Of course, fully describing his pride may require noting a concomitant feeling of accomplishment, or perhaps a spine-tingling sensation—or even a sense of unusual bodily vigor and energy. But these further factors seem not to be leading the way in determining the distinctive nature of the emotion. Whether taken in isolation (a *mere* spine-tingling or an isolated surge of bodily energy) or together (a spine-tingling accompanied by a surge of energy), they seem unlikely candidates for fixing the identity and nature of the emotion itself. They are emotion-related factors only because they are typically found accompanying suitable belief-desire complexes.

Attitudes are more easily understood given this analysis of emotion, since on my understanding attitudes are belief-desire complexes which typically get their names from the emotions those beliefs and desires help constitute. Let us (informally again) dissect the concept of an attitude as follows:

ATT: An attitude is a mental state which typically involves some combination of (e) and (f):

---

[5]For a full-dress defense of cognitive theories, see William Lyons, *Emotion*, especially Chapter 4.

(e) a consciously or unconsciously held set of beliefs directed towards some particular thing or kind of thing

(f) a consciously or unconsciously held set of desires directed towards some particular thing or kind of thing.

Again we have a distinction between occurrent and dispositional attitudes. I can be occurrently harboring a resentful attitude towards my negligent parents, but I might instead merely hold this attitude dispositionally. I hold it dispositionally when, for example, I am at the moment gleefully enjoying some fun procured for me by one of their foolish spending sprees, but deep inside I know I shall later come occurrently to resent their short-sighted financial frivolity.

One important difference between EMO's conditions (a) and (b) (the belief and desire conditions on emotions) and ATT's (e) and (f) is the "towards" element explicitly required of attitude-related beliefs and desires. Recall that (a) and (b) left open the possibility that the emotion be "objectless": Thus such "moods" as a vague apprehension of impending doom counted as emotions since neither the desires nor the beliefs involved were required to lock in on any particular thing as their focus.

I take it there is no such thing as an objectless attitude. An attitude can only be understood as a perspective *on something*. When the beliefs and desires involved in an emotion have this directedness towards an object, they can be viewed as forming an attitude which borrows its name from the emotion. Thus, given that Jones is proud, we can either say, taking a view of his overall condition, that he is in the emotional state of pride or, taking a narrower view of his mental perspective, that he has a haughty (prideful) attitude about his publication. Similarly, when I find myself rejoicing inwardly at the news that Jack Becker was just in a serious car accident I can equally be said to be in an emotional state of *Schadenfreude*, or malicious pleasure, and to have a malicious attitude towards Becker.

In place of a full defense of ATT I just note that most attitudes in fact seem to have cognitive and appetitive features.[6] Jones's arrogant attitude seems plausibly characterized as the combination of the beliefs involved in his understanding how much prestige he enjoys as one who has published in the *Review*, together with his desire for that kind of exclusive recognition. Similarly, my malicious attitude of "I'm glad you were almost killed" towards Jack Becker seems to involve beliefs about Becker (for example, that he has inconvenienced me and that he himself was just seriously injured), as well as a central desire that harm come to him.

I want now to find a principled way of limiting our attention to just those emotions and attitudes which have an ethical dimension. The work we have already done on moral desires comes in handy for this purpose. For I maintain that the moral flavor of emotions and attitudes is due in large part to the moral flavor inherent in their constituent desires.[7] For example, in the case of my malicious pleasure, the evil of the pleasure seems clearly to be due to the evil of the desire that harm come to Becker: If I had not wrongly wanted Becker to be harmed, I would not wrongly have found pleasure in his being harmed. Thus I shall take a *moral emotion* to be an emotion whose set of desires constrains at least one moral desire, and a *moral attitude* to be an attitude whose set of desires contains at least one moral desire. All of the examples used above in fact (assuming the conditions specified in [2″] are met) have at least one moral desire among the relevant desires. In each of those cases, then, we were discussing moral emotions and attitudes, which, like the desires which partly constitute them, were in some degree open to blame or praise. For ease of exposition, hereafter the terms "desire," "emotion," and "attitude," will, unless otherwise noted, be taken to pick out

---

[6]Even a sceptical attitude might involve a desire not to believe except on exceedingly clear evidence, though it may be more difficult to find a relevant appetite associated with an attitude of indifference or sarcasm.

[7]In some cases beliefs might contribute some of the moral dimension. For example, perhaps the belief that Jews do not have any human rights helps make the feelings of approval at seeing them die morally heinous. For a discussion of how beliefs might have this status, see Adams, "Involuntary Sins," pp. 18-21 and his paper "The Virtue of Faith," *Faith and Philosophy* 1 (1984):4-6. Alvin Plantinga also discusses this briefly in "Reason and Belief in God," in *Faith and Rationality: Reason and Belief in God*, ed. Alvin Plantinga and Nicholas Wolterstorff (Notre Dame: University of Notre Dame Press, 1983), pp. 34-37.

moral desires, emotions, and attitudes, even though they stand alone without the prefix "moral."

Notice that desires "color" emotions and attitudes in more ways than by passing their moral status on to them. The *strength* of desires is quite often reflected in the relative vivacity and intensity of those states of mind. Given an acute and gripping desire that Becker be harmed, my *Schadenfreude* is likely to be a captivating and persistent experience. By contrast, vanishingly weak reactions are to be expected if I am indifferent to the prognosis on Becker's future well-being. Aquinas notices this point. He claims that "it is the nature of love that the lover will and seek [that is, desire] the good of the one he loves." He then assumes that desiring the good of the beloved entails desiring unity with the beloved, and adds, "the more that through which the lover is one with the one he loves is greater, the more is the love intense."[8]

There is also the fact that a positive/negative polarity in desires is clearly reflected in emotions and attitudes. When what I want to happen happens, overall pleasant emotions and positive attitudes are to be expected, since the guiding evaluation is one to the effect that the situation is desirable. When what I want not to happen happens, unpleasant or negative states of mind are in store because I judge the circumstances undesirable. Thus if Jones had received the dreaded postcard notifying him of his article's rejection rather than an acceptance letter, he would likely have formed a negative attitude (perhaps towards the *Review* editors) and unpleasant emotions like discouragement and disappointment. Aquinas notes this fact when he writes that "from the fact that we love something we desire that thing if it be absent; we rejoice, of course, if it be present; and we are sad when we are kept from it."[9]

Finally, desires combine with beliefs to give attitudes and emotions a *focus*. For example, Jones's pride focuses on his distinctive accomplishment by comparison with other philosophers because his relevant beliefs and desires focus on just this

---

[8]St. Thomas Aquinas, *Summa contra gentiles*, ed. Anton C. Pegis (Notre Dame: University of Notre Dame Press, 1975), Bk. I, Chap. 91, Sec. 4 (pp. 277-78).

[9]Ibid., Bk. IV (ed. Charles J. O'Neil), Chap. 19, Sec. 3 (p. 117). See also Jonathan Bennett, *A Study of Spinoza's 'Ethics'* (Indianapolis: Hackett Publishing Co., 1984), p. 270, where Bennett points out that a positive/negative polarity in desires causes a similar polarity in feelings.

comparison. Similarly, my malicious attitude is directed towards Becker because my beliefs and desires revolve around *his* well-being.

There is a firm connection here between what I have been calling the focus of desires and doctrines about teleology which issue from the older ancient and medieval tradition. In that tradition, appetites focus on the ends pursued. Thus what we are calling a desire's focus is roughly equivalent to a final cause—the goal towards which the item with a desire is striving.

Notice that putting the matter in terms of goal-directedness helps us explain from another angle why the nature of one's desires is often a useful guide in determining the contours of one's moral character. These desires presuppose goals which the self has adopted as its goals. My strivings are strivings towards ends I have countenanced as permissible. Thus, when the desire's goal is morally offensive, as it is in the case where I set my heart on harm coming to Becker, the desire itself is naturally implicated in that offensiveness.[10]

Recall that failure to manifest one's moral character was one of the conditions which could absolve the blame otherwise due someone harboring a bad desire. This concept of an end goal shows that we can appeal to more than vague intuitions when explaining how we distinguish desires which manifest moral character from those which do not. The desires that do represent the pursuit of distinctively moral ends; the desires that do not pursue other ends. In the example given above, my choice to develop in myself the desire to work on this paper was not moral so long as the end I had in view was simply to satisfy a sudden whimsical feeling of writer's abandon. It took on a moral dimension only when my goal was a moral one—namely, that of obeying God in this matter.

In this section I have shown that desires play a central role in determining the moral status of those emotions and attitudes which have such status. It is important now to

---

[10]I shall not quarrel with C.S. Lewis, who, in "The Inner Ring," in *The Weight of Glory and Other Addresses* (Grand Rapids, MI: Wm. B. Eerdmans Publishing Co., 1949), pp. 59-60, says the desire to be in the "inner ring" is wrong even though the desire's goal (of being special friends with our fellows) may be morally good or morally neutral. I am only claiming that *typically* the goal's wrongness is a central factor in explaining why the desire is wrong.

address the issue of how, from a meta-ethical point of view, the ethical dimension of these states of mind can be explained.

HOW STATES OF MIND CAN HAVE MORAL STATUS

By "meta-ethics" I mean, not exclusively the study of the meanings of ethical terms, but rather the whole range of metaphysical questions about things ethical. I want briefly to raise the question, in virtue of what are moral desires, attitudes, and emotions moral? To give our inquiry a focus, we shall concentrate on answering one question about one particular moral desire—namely, malice. Why is malice wrong?

Immediately there is a problem with putting the question that way. As we have seen, it matters whether this is my malice towards Becker (which presumably survives the "*prima facie* test" for blame) or if instead we have in mind Bonhoeffer's malice, which does not survive that test. In the Jack Becker case, the harm he has inflicted on me is not serious enough to justify my malice, whereas in the Bonhoeffer case the malice seems fully justified.

So we must sharpen our question to, why is my malice towards Jack Becker wrong? One consequentialist answer to this would be that it is wrong because it will likely give rise to evil actions or upshots—for example, snubbing Becker or relentlessly jeering at or sarcastically abusing him when he should be treated compassionately and with forgiveness. The consequentialist could go on to claim that these upshots are inherently evil. This would make my malice evil in a singly derivative sense—that is, the desire is evil because the consequences it typically leads on to are inherently evil. A *utilitarian consequentialist* could make it doubly derivative by saying the consequences are themselves only derivatively evil since in the long run they affect negatively the inherently good goal of creating the greatest amount of good in the world. A *divine command consequentialist* might also make my malice's evil doubly derivative by claiming that since God condemns the outcomes of snubbing, jeering at, and abusing someone who has done me wrong, any desire which sets itself the task of carrying out such upshots is wrong because doing what God condemns is inherently wrong. Notice that none of these consequentialists attributes inherent badness to my malice. It is bad only because it typically leads on to bad things.

Deontologists would also claim that my malice is derivatively evil—this time with respect to duty. On a *Kantian* view, not abiding by Duty is inherently evil, and since cultivating malice flagrantly violates Duty, it is singly derivatively evil for that reason. A *divine command deontology* would push this to a doubly derivative evil, since violating my duty would itself be derivatively evil relative to the inherent evil involved in disobeying God's command to do my duty.

When we turn to the third main alternative—the "ethics of virtue" tradition—we finally find one which has the theoretical resources for explaining the evil of my malice as an *inherent* moral feature. The virtue theorist simply says that malice against Becker is a bad character trait. My harboring malice in my heart indicates that something is wrong with my moral make-up. While my malice's evil may be partly explained by reference to likely consequences or conflicts with duty, there is, quite independently of those factors, a left-over fragment of wrongness which attaches to the malice itself. This fragment represents the fact that it is just wrong to *be* malicious.

Of course, there are various versions of the virtue view. The most promising from the standpoint of the Christian life are, I think, theistic versions. Let us examine two of them. Both of these agree with the generic virtue theory just described in holding that part of the wrongness attaches to the malice itself irrespective of consequences and duties. But the theistic versions give up the secular theorist's claim that the wrongness in question is an inherent feature. They say instead that my malice is derivatively evil by reference either to God's character or to His commands. *Divine character virtue ethics* says it is inconsistent with God's own character—which is inherently morally perfect—to be malicious. My malice is thus a singly derivatively evil character trait because it does not match up with God's moral character.[11] *Divine command virtue ethics* holds that malice is a singly derivatively evil character trait by reference to God's commands that humans should not be malicious.

---

[11]For a discussion of how goodness can consist of being in line with God's character, see William P. Alston, "What Euthyphro Should Have Said," (unpublished draft, 1987). The qualities of being loving, just, and merciful are said to be good "by virtue of being features of God" (p. 18), and "The divine *nature*, apart from anything God has willed or done, is sufficient to determine what counts as good, including morally good" (p. 21).

I think there is evidence in Christian tradition to support both of these views, and I shall not argue in favor of one over the other. The divine character version gets ample support from a story like that about Jonah, which shows that God's character is free of malice and that instead God is compassionate towards those in trouble. Obviously Jonah's central problem is his refusal to allow the divine virtues of forgiveness and compassion to grow up in his own heart. In addition, there is the familiar theme that God is not willing that any should perish, but wants all to come to repentance (II Peter 3:9). This, combined with frequent reminders that the goal of Christian living is to imitate God—to cultivate "godliness"—to the greatest extent possible, establishes the plausibility of the divine character version.

With regard to the divine command version, there are several places where Christians are explicitly commanded not to be malicious. St. Paul writes, "Get rid of all bitterness, rage and anger, brawling and slander, along with every form of malice" (Ephesians 4:31, New International Version) and reiterates this again in the form of a command in Colossians 3:8. And St. Peter requires his readers to "rid yourselves of all malice and all deceit . . ." (I Peter 2:1). Notice that an evil desire like malice is listed right alongside evil emotions and attitudes like anger and bitterness. So clearly we can treat evil emotions and attitudes also as character traits unmanifested in God or condemned by God.

Of course, someone could use this same textual evidence to develop consequentialist and deontological underpinnings for the claim that states of mind can have moral status. I am not going to do that here, since my concern is simply to establish that this can be done plausibly in some way or other. I think the divine character/command virtue views represent the most natural way of construing the Christian ethical perspective on desires, emotions, and attitudes. So I shall from here onwards adopt an idiom suitable to those views.

THERAPY THROUGH BELIEFS, DESIRES, AND MASTER DESIRES

One caveat before we begin this section. Throughout it I am going to talk as if living the Christian life were all "up to us." That is, I am not going to pepper the text with acknowledgements of our need for the Holy Spirit to be at work in the process of renewal which I am describing. This should not be misunderstood: I certainly recognize that true Christian growth requires the work of the Spirit. Here, however, I want to fix the spotlight on what *we* can do to enhance the Spirit's leading in our lives.

Since we often discover within ourselves sinful rather than righteous desires, emotions, and attitudes, the question arises, how might we come to have a higher percentage of virtuous states of mind? Let us begin by concentrating on emotions and attitudes, and then handle desires in our discussion of master desires.

At least in principle there are two direct ways one might set about to sanctify one's attitudes and emotions. One might strive to change the relevant desires, or one could instead work on the beliefs.

Let us select an example which is central to everyday Christian living. My failing to trust God is constituted by my desire to guarantee my future prosperity, together with the belief that the prospect (the possibility of which I cannot rule out) of losing my job, my wife, or other ingredients of such prosperity is undesirable. The longer I contemplate the possibility of losing them, the more my lack of trust is likely to lead on to doubt, worry, and fear. These states of mind are not good because God commands us to avoid them. I can try to turn my spiritual condition around by changing the desire: I might attempt to substitute a desire to be content with "whatsoever state I am in" for my old desire. Or I can begin work on the belief component by reminding myself of God's promise to provide for my every need.

Neither of these projects is easy to pull off because not much in our appetitive and cognitive lives is under direct voluntary control. Desires are especially difficult to affect except through long-term "conditioning." So the first method is of limited practical value.

The second is more promising and may even serve as an indirect means of executing the first. My beliefs about the importance of guaranteed future prosperity might change if I expose myself—say, by reading the Bible or listening to sermons—to evidence which shows that the amount of responsibility I am taking to ensure that prosperity is too great. The result will not be immediate, since doubts and reservations will typically keep me from giving full assent to the Christian views. But gradually I shall acquire God's perspective of those matters. In the short run such "cognitive therapy" will relieve anxiety, and in the long run may effect "appetitive therapy" by undercutting the beliefs (like "*I* must watch out for myself and do everything *I* can to guarantee *my* future prosperity") which sustain the relevant desires. Eventually I may even find myself able to meet such challenges as financial hardship with the same virtuous attitude as those believers who "joyfully accepted the confiscation of [their] property," because they knew that they "had better and lasting possessions" (Hebrews 10:34).

But if all one can do is to revamp states of mind piecemeal by changing individual desires and beliefs, the process would take a long time and would be difficult to integrate. Is there some "shortcut" method which could, in a single step, morally upgrade a whole raft of emotions and attitudes—as well as desires?

I think there is. It requires developing appropriate *master desires*. Master desires are desires which act as one's guiding perspective on life; they are the appetitive side of one's answer to the query, "What is the meaning of life?" From this description alone it is clear that master desires are moral desires: they embody the ultimate direction of one's moral life. Master desires give a peculiar twist to the full range of lower-level appetites—moral as well as non-moral ones. They orient them towards certain ultimate goals which look beyond the more short-ranged goal the lower-level desires envision. In terms of the older tradition's emphasis on ends, we can say that master desires set their sights on the most ethically momentous ends.

It seems clear that one's natural master desire is selfishness. Selfishness lends a certain ultimacy to such lower-level desires as the desire for sex, the search for financial security, and the longing for esteem and power. Of them it demands unflinching allegiance to the singular goal of enhancing the self. Under its unbridled dictatorship they are distorted until they become lust, greed, pride, and ambition. In lust and greed the self enjoys an inordinate priority over other competing interests; in pride one estimates one's own worth too highly; ambition turns a deaf ear to the cries of those trampled under foot in one's rush to seize power. Being controlled by a selfish master desire is roughly equivalent to what in Christian tradition is referred to as bondage to one's self or to "the flesh."

Having said that, you know the solution I am going to recommend: strip the selfish master desire of its command and instead put a master desire centered on pleasing God to work supervising the subordinate desires. This will imbue the full range of lower-level desires with a meaning and purpose they did not have while under the whip of selfishness. Lust will be transformed to self-control, greed to generosity, and contentment with one's current possessions; pride will be replaced by humility, and ambition by zeal for God's values and kingdom. The process involved in turning things around is well described by C. S. Lewis:

> Christ says 'Give me All. I don't want so much of your time and so much of your money and so much of your work: I want You. I have not come to torment your natural self, but to kill it. No half-measures are any good. . . . I don't want to drill the tooth, or crown it, or stop it, but to have it out. Hand over the whole natural self, all the desires which you think innocent as well as the ones you think wicked—the whole outfit. I will give you a new self instead. In fact, I will give you Myself: my own will shall become yours.'[12]

Nothing less than a complete overhaul of our appetitive faculties is called for. It will not do to rout out all but a small vestige of our original selfishness and then let *that* become our controlling motivation: God wants to eradicate the old motive and replace it with a new desire to live for His glory.

Of course, one can go overboard in downplaying the self. We must find a balance between, on the one hand, resolute selfishness and pride and, on the other, self-deprecation or total loss of self-esteem. How do we maintain a happy equilibrium between these two undesirable extremes? One way, I suggest, is to take on God's perspective of us as His children. In light of God's holiness, I realize that I am sinful and in need of God's salvation. *But*, lest I quickly capitulate to self-denigration, guilt, and depression, I also see myself as supremely loved by that same holy God: I remember the many promises of faithful care God has given me. It is not a surviving vestige of my old sinful selfishness and pride which constitutes my self-esteem; it is a brand-new perspective of myself as a child of God. This has a combined humbling and strengthening effect—just the mixture we need to protect us from the upper extreme of pride and from the lower limit of belittling ourselves.

---

[12]C.S. Lewis, *Mere Christianity* (New York: Macmillan Publishing Co., 1943), p. 167. Also see Lewis's interesting exploration in "The Inner Ring," of the moral status of the desire for the esoteric companionship peculiar to members of the "inner ring." This could be seen as an intermediate-level desire which takes command of a particular set of lower-level desires and which is itself under the command of the overall selfish master desire.

Self-denigration threatens our self-esteem, but it can also give us unrealistic expectations for the process of sanctification. Proponents of the "total depravity" view of human nature tell us there is nothing good in the natural self, that *all* there is "mutilated, confused, and disease-ridden."[13] Even the passage from Lewis could be interpreted (at least in isolation from his other writings[14]) along these lines, since he says that not a single natural desire can remain: one must do away with the "whole outfit."

This position is dangerous because it suggests a picture of Christians as people who have nothing in common with non-Christians, whose desires, attitudes, and emotions are so totally different from what they would be if they were not Christians that nothing remains of their natural endowment after conversion. But that seems false, since the finishing touches of the mature walk with God are added when our lower level, naturally virtuous desires are also caught up in this new dimension. As we might say in an Hegelian tone, all that is virtuous in them is preserved and heightened when they are taken up into a more ultimate context, a context in which we want to do what we naturally wanted to do anyway *because* God approves of that natural desire. Thus, for

---

[13]John Calvin, *Institutes of the Christian Religion*, trans. Ford Lewis Battles, ed. John T. McNeill (Philadelphia: Westminster Press, 1960), Bk. I. Chap. 15, Sec. 4 (Vol. I, p. 190). Calvin mitigates this somewhat, however, when he acknowledges (Bk. I, Chap. 3, Sec. 1 [Vol. I, p. 43]) that within the human mind there is a natural "awareness of divinity."

[14]Lewis seems to deny this implication in the very same work—*Mere Christianity*—when he says on p. 143 that the Christian "is being caught up into the higher kind of life . . . : he is being pulled into God, by God, while still remaining himself." He also seems to turn against it when he expresses concern over Christians who "accept in certain forms the doctrine of total depravity," since they are apt wrongly to adopt a hatred of "selves as such"—in his "Two Ways with the Self," in C.S. Lewis, *God in the Dock: Essays on Theology and Ethics*, ed. Walter Hooper (Grand Rapids, MI: Wm. B. Eerdmans Publishing Co., 1970), pp. 193-95. Also see C.S. Lewis, "Learning in War-Time," in *The Weight of Glory*, pp. 43-54, where he says (pp. 48-49), "Christianity does not simply replace our natural life and substitute a new one: it is rather a new organization which exploits, to its own supernatural ends, these natural materials . . . . An appetite for [knowledge and beauty] exists in the human mind, and God makes no appetite in vain. We can therefore pursue knowledge as such, and beauty, as such, in the sure confidence that by so doing we are either advancing to the vision of God ourselves or indirectly helping others to do so." He returns to this theme in

example, the desire to enhance the quality of my wife's life comes naturally to me, but that natural desire can be transformed, under the influence of my new God-centered master desire, into the same desire strengthened by the realization that this is just one of several desires which contribute to fulfilling my overall desire to please Him. My original lower level desire is enhanced and enriched with new meaning because it helps fulfill a higher, more ultimate calling. And so it goes throughout the repertoire of our good native desires—they are caught up in and transformed by the overall context of a life devoted to pleasing God.

A properly stationed self—one which sees itself as subordinate to God—leads to true godliness and thus to mature morality and full integrity. In particular, it helps us sanctify our desires, emotions, and attitudes. This "shortcut" method is by no means easy, but it does in a relatively brief time what would take years to accomplish by working on states of mind one at a time. Lewis elegantly expresses the practical side of this method when he writes,

> . . . the real problem of the Christian life . . . comes the very moment you wake up each morning. All your wishes and hopes for the day rush at you like wild animals. And the first job each morning consists simply in shoving them all back; in listening to that other voice, taking that other point of view, letting that other larger, stronger, quieter life come flowing in. And so on, all day. Standing back from all your natural fussings and frettings; coming in out of the wind.[15]

One must invest one's self "to the hilt" in God's values and in God's responses to one's desires, emotions, and attitudes. One must fall in love with a spirit of obedience to a Self not one's own. There lies the path to appetitive, emotional, and attitudinal redemption and renewal.

Weight of Glory," in *The Weight of Glory*, pp. 1-15, where he says our natural child-like desire to be rewarded for our work is the very same desire which is finally satisfied in the most ultimate sense when we hear the words, "well done, thou good and faithful servant."

[15]Lewis, *Mere Christianity*, pp. 168-69.

VIRTUE AND RULES

One interesting upshot of this study—here considered only briefly—is that the rules Christians are obliged to follow have to do not only with what they should strive to *do*, but also with what desires and beliefs they should strive to *have*. This implies that the following rules are likely to be included in any complete spelling-out of Christian ethics:

Rule 1: Cultivate beliefs about God's value system, goals, purposes, character traits, and so on.

For example, by obeying Rule 1, Christians will increase the likelihood that they will manifest faith, courage, and peace in the midst of stress, since they will have vividly in mind beliefs which provide a divine perspective on the situation. In addition, there is

Rule 2: Cultivate desires which are in line with God's character or commands.

Again when we cultivate a desire to forgive rather than to seek revenge, we are in a much better position to have morally healthy attitudes and emotions towards those who harm us. And of course, stemming from the discussion of master desires there is

Rule 3: Replace one's natural selfish master desire with a master desire centered on pleasing God.

One practical outcome of seeing these as ethical rules is that we are reminded of the importance of meditation and prayer as ways of orienting our *minds* towards God. It seems that often too much emphasis is given to the need to orient our behavior in the direction of Christian principles. The root of the matter instead often lies in the condition of the heart behind the behavior. The virtue tradition never lost sight of this fact, and thus some version of its doctrines is an essential component in any complete Christian ethic.

I began by taking issue with St. Paul over the status of love. I want now to clarify my position. Love is partly constituted by a desire to share in and enhance—possibly at the cost of great sacrifice—another's life. This desire is itself a central Christian virtue since it is one essentially manifested in and explicitly commanded by God. An emotional state of love or a loving attitude, then, has surpassing moral merit and greatness in large part due to the fact that this desire colors it with *its* exceedingly great moral merit and greatness. Thus the moral character of love-related desires is crucial in helping to explain the supreme ethical significance of Christian love.[16]

---

[16]I wish to thank Terry J. Christlieb, Kristine Christlieb, Robert D. Freeman, Thomas A. Stevens, William P. Alston, and Robert M. Adams for their helpful comments on earlier drafts of this paper.

CONTRIBUTORS

Steven Bilynskyj

B.A. Westmont College; M.A., Ph.D. University of Notre Dame; M.Div. North Park Seminary; Pastor, First Evangelical Church, Lincoln, Nebraska

William Craig

B.A. Wheaton College; M.A. Trinity Evangelical Divinity School; Ph.D. University of Birmingham; D. Theol. Universitat Munchen; Associated with Westmont College and Universitat Catholique du Louvain

Howard M. Durchame

B.A. Hope College; M.A. Trinity Evangelical Divinity School; D.Phil. Oxford University; Assistant Professor of Philosophy and Coordinator of the Biomedical Ethics Program, University of Akron

C. Stephen Evans

B.A. Wheaton College; M.Phil., Ph.D. Yale University; Professor of Philosophy and Curator of the Hong Kierkegaard Library, St. Olaf College

Glenn Hartz

B.A. Kings College, M.A. Trinity Evangelical Divinity School; M.S., Ph.D. Syracuse University; Assistant professor of Philosophy, The Ohio State University, Mansfield

Arthur Holmes

B.A., M.A. Wheaton College; Ph.D. Northwestern University; Professor of Philosophy, Wheaton College

William F. Lawhead

B.A. Wheaton College, Ph.D. University of Texas, Austin; Professor of Philosophy, University of Mississippi, Oxford

Robert Tad Lehe

B.A. Wheaton College; M.A. Northern Illinois University; Ph.D. University of Chicago; Assistant Professor of Philosophy, North Central College

Mark Linville

B.A. Florida Christian College; M.A. Cincinnati Christian Seminary; M.A. Trinity Evangelical Divinity School; Ph.D. candidate University of Wisconsin, Madison; Visiting Instructor, Trinity Evangelical Divinity School

Pat Manfredi

B.A. Wheaton College; M.A., Ph.D. University of Notre Dame; Assistant Professor of Philosophy, Hamilton College

Mark S. McLeod

B.A. Westmont College; M.A. Trinity Evangelical Divinity School; M.A., Ph.D. University of California, Santa Barbara; Assistant Professor of Philosophy, Westmont College

Robert Prevost

B.A. Baylor University; M.A. Trinity Evangelical Divinity School; D.Phil. Oxford University; formerly Assistant Professor of Philosophy, University of Texas, Arlington; now a law student at the University of Texas, Austin

Donna Summerfield

B.A. Wheaton College; M.A. Ph.D. University of Notre Dame; Assistant Professor of Philosophy, Hamilton College

Jay Wood

B.A. Westmont College; M.A., Ph.D., University of Notre Dame; Assistant Professor of Philosophy, Wheaton College

PROBLEMS IN CONTEMPORARY PHILOSOPHY